THE APOLLO MISSIONS

THE APOLLO MISSIONS

THE INCREDIBLE STORY OF THE RACE TO THE MOON

DAVID BAKER

ARCTURUS

DEDICATION

The author wishes to remember geologist Ewen Whitaker, astrophysicist Thomas "Tommy" Gold and planetologist Bruce Murray, friends who influenced and guided him in his years working with NASA.

AUTHOR'S NOTE

Readers should note that all distances in this book in Imperial units refer to the statute mile of 5,280ft, rather than the nautical mile of 6,060ft which NASA used in its official Apollo reports. Discrepancies are a result of that conversion, which the author believes may be a more familiar unit of measurement.

Page 2: Seen in perspective from orbit, Earth's thin blue atmosphere supports all life. From this planet, one species evolved to fly through the veil that is proportionately thinner than the skin on an apple, to visit another celestial body in space.

Pages 4–5: The infinite vastness of space viewed from orbit, containing destinations for humans to explore – a journey beyond Earth that was begun by Apollo missions to the Moon.

Page 6: Apollo 11 taking off from the Kennedy Space Center launch pad on the morning of 16 July 1969.

ARCTURUS

This edition published in 2019 by Arcturus Publishing Limited
26/27 Bickels Yard, 151–153 Bermondsey Street,
London SE1 3HA

ISBN: 978-1-78888-523-2
AD006626UK

Printed in China

CONTENTS

INTRODUCTION

On 16 July 1969 a giant rocket weighing as much a US Navy Destroyer lifted off from the Kennedy Space Center, Florida, and propelled three astronauts into the history books. Their target was the Moon, but their destination was enduring recognition far beyond their lifetimes as the first humans to walk on the surface of another celestial body.

The flight of Apollo 11 was a seminal moment in the story of modern humanity, when for totally political purposes a nascent agency instigated by a US president for the peaceful exploration of space was itself propelled into one of the most audacious acts of the 20th century. The mission was both bold and adventurous, appealing to the desire for new lands to conquer and new regions of space to explore. A successful landing was accomplished six times, with a rich harvest of rocks and samples gathered together that helped explain the story of the Earth and its orbiting satellite, the Moon.

The outcome of the Apollo programme provided so much more than just dust and rocks – it spawned a new awareness of Earth's fragility. On viewing pictures of the Earth from a distance, the writer Archibald MacLeish perceived our planet as floating like a blue marble in the velvet blackness of space, and proclaimed that we are all "brothers who know now they are truly brothers… riders on the Earth together." The new vantage point also prompted the environmentalist Barbara Ward to write her book Only One Earth, still a seminal account of a planet in crisis.

All of this came from the Apollo Missions – and more besides. The technology that took Armstrong, Aldrin and Collins to the Moon underpinned a flowering of talent, capability, discovery and invention practised by an industry that can now provide the tools for defining the nature of our Earth in crisis. Without the exotic satellites that emerged from Apollo technology, for instance, we would never have discovered the ozone layer, provided instruments in orbit to monitor the planet in unprecedented detail, or heralded global communications, the Internet and the information age.

Anything we make of all this is in our own hands; we cannot blame technology for our failure to use it for good. The enduring legacy of the Cold War Space Race is that now, in the 21st century, former protagonists have come together to staff a 450-tonne orbiting laboratory – the International Space Station – to conduct research into the fundamental building blocks of life, create new vaccines, better understand the ageing process in Earth-bound humans, and even conduct experiments into the very fabric of matter itself.

The flight of Apollo 11 will never be forgotten – it bequeathed to this and future generations a much-changed world. We have not only gained the knowledge we need to better understand the Earth–Moon system, but we are also now able to approach global and environmental challenges with the same vision that allowed humans to transform their imagination into reality 50 years ago.

David Baker

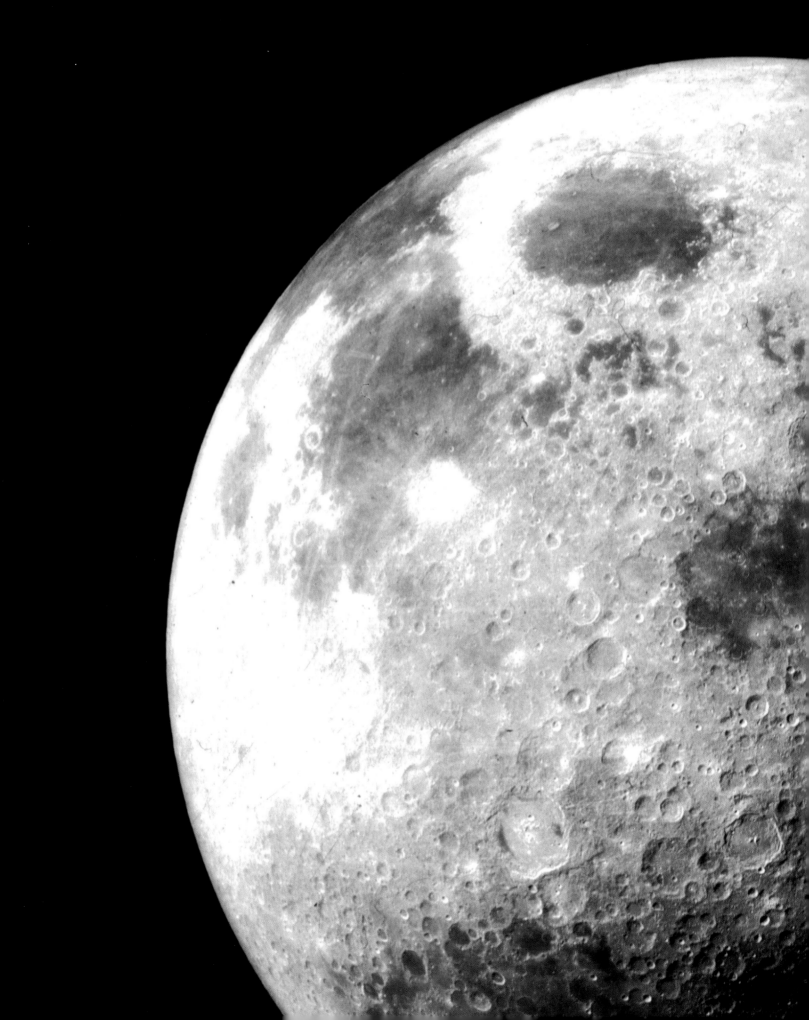

CHAPTER 1

WHY GO TO THE MOON?

It was Thursday, 25 May 1961 when John F. Kennedy, barely four months into his presidency of the United States, was driven the short distance across Washington, DC from the White House to the Capitol to deliver an address before a Joint Session of Congress. Such events were not rare but hardly common. He was there to deliver a speech on "Urgent National Needs" and it was to be a seminal moment in the history of the world. Only a few knew what he was about to say.

Opposite: *The lunar sphere, not as viewed from Earth but from a spacecraft coming around the right-hand limb looking back partly at the far side. From whichever angle, the Moon has unified artists, musicians, poets, scientists and engineers.*

Left: *A 40-kopek Russian stamp commemorates the launch of Sputnik, "first in the world", a symbol of Soviet success to a nation recovering from having lost more of its people during the Second World War than all the other combatant nations combined.*

Kennedy's oration began by reminding his audience that these were "extraordinary times", and that the United States was living under the terrible threat of Communist hegemony, while affirming that the United States was "not against any man – or any nation – or any system – except as it is hostile to freedom." For a while his speech centred on the need for a strong economy, and for support to vulnerable nations seeking independence and freedom from autocracy, describing the United States' role as to "preserve and promote the ideals that we share with all mankind."

Not for some time did he focus in on his actual theme, directing his audience to the new age of space, albeit barely into its fourth year, declaring it to be "an adventure on the minds of men everywhere, who are attempting to make a determination of which road they should take." He continued, "… we have examined where we are strong and where we are not, where we may succeed and where we may not. Now it is time to take longer strides – time for a great new American enterprise – time for this nation to take a clearly leading role in space achievement, which in many ways may hold the key to our future on Earth."

After explaining that US leadership had been lacking and that "our eagerness to share its meaning is not governed by the efforts of others", Kennedy came to the reason they were all there, to issue a challenge so monumental that no one, anywhere, had full knowledge of how to achieve it: "I believe that this nation should commit itself to achieving the goal, before this decade is out, of landing a man on the Moon and returning him safely to the Earth. No single space project in this period will be more impressive to mankind, or more important for the long-range exploration of space; and none will be so difficult or expensive to accomplish."

Left: *On 25 May 1961 President Kennedy addresses a joint session of Congress in the House of Representatives to proclaim the national goal of landing a man on the Moon by the end of the decade. Vice President Lyndon B. Johnson is behind him on the left, and Sam Rayburn, Speaker of the House, is on the right. In 1958 Johnson had pushed through the bill founding NASA and three years later orchestrated the decision to go for the Moon.*

A PLACE FOR DREAMERS

From time immemorial, the Moon had played an important role in art, music, fiction and romance. Now it was to be the tip of a technological virility pole stretching all the way from the United States to the Moon's dusty surface, upon which could be planted the flag of political and ideological supremacy. If achieved, this would send a clear signal to the rest of the world that the United States had passed the Soviet Union in the Space Race and would go on to achieve even greater things in science, technology and engineering; an invitation to coalesce around a winning ideology of political democracy and industrial capitalism.

In declaring the Moon goal, Kennedy saw it in precisely that light, imbuing it with a certain romanticism, seeking to race the Soviet Union for technological supremacy over distant worlds, demonstrating to politically uncommitted nations that the system of government espoused by the United States was capable of accepting any challenge, meeting any goal – and winning. Paradoxically, Kennedy would always deny that he had launched the United States on a race to the Moon. But in reality, he had, prompted by the connection which had already become entrenched in public thinking: that technological superiority was a yardstick by which to measure the progress of a nation.

It was also a direct response to a survey conducted quietly in major cities around the world in which ordinary citizens were asked which country they rated as most likely to be the pre-eminent nation of the future. Before the launch of the Soviet Yuri Gagarin, who on 12 April 1961 became the world's first spaceman, the United States was generally considered the top nation in terms of human progress. Within a week of that momentous event, however, right across Europe except in the UK, the Soviet Union was propelled to top spot in public opinion. France, Germany, Italy and Belgium believed the Soviet Union would very quickly outstrip the United States. This was a shock to Americans – at least those who knew of this survey, carried out by the US Information Service through its embassies. But the results were probably not surprising, given that already, on 4 October 1957, the Soviet Union had become the first country to place an artificial satellite (known as Sputnik) in orbit in space – followed a month later by a second satellite, carrying a dog named Laika, the first living thing to orbit the Earth.

The challenge facing a flagging United States was all the more poignant since one of President Kennedy's main campaign promises before he was voted into office in November 1960 was never again to let the country suffer an embarrassing technological defeat by the Soviet Union. More than one newspaper equated the embarrassment of Gagarin's flight to the United States' "second Pearl Harbor moment". Yet, ironically, it was because the Soviet Union put the first spaceman into orbit that the Moon challenge was laid down by Kennedy, for if the United States had been first in sending one of its astronauts into space, honour would have been satisfied.

It had been a close thing. NASA – the United States' National Aeronautics and Space Administration – opened for business on 1 October 1958, one year after Sputnik, the result of the US political élite's decision to set up a civilian space agency that would also be an arm of the government, with programmes and projects directed towards making the United States great in space. This new agency had a pedigree, for it grew out of the National Advisory Committee for Aeronautics (NACA), which had been formed in 1915 to spearhead US research into the new science of aeronautics and to carry out wind-tunnel tests on wing shapes and fuselage forms.

Above: *Born in March 1934 on a collective farm in the village of Klushino, Yuri Gagarin was drafted into the Soviet Army in 1955 and selected for cosmonaut training five years later. After making history as the first man into space on 12 April 1961, he was refused permission to fly another space mission and died in an aircraft accident on 27 March 1968.*

Supporting industry for 42 years, the NACA underpinned US aeronautical progress with industrial demand during World War II, providing technological capabilities to develop the tools for an overwhelming application of force in helping defeat Nazi Germany and Imperial Japan between December 1941 and August 1945. It had also been instrumental in pushing development of a civil aviation industry, which by the beginning of the war in Europe in 1939 had outclassed that of any other country, including providing research tests for flying boats, seaplanes and long-range airliners.

After the war, the NACA immediately began research into high-flying aircraft and high-speed projects, and was instrumental in supporting the US Air Force to push the Bell X-1 through the sound barrier when "Chuck" Yeager passed Mach 1 (the speed of sound) in October 1947. The NACA was also interested in rocket research, but the United States had wasted two decades since March 1926 when Dr Robert Goddard became the first man to fire a liquid propellant rocket, from a cabbage patch at Auburn, Massachusetts, opening a door to space propulsion that only liquid motors could initially provide.

DESTINY AMONG THE STARS

During the 1930s, science fiction had been furtive ground for comic-book writers and film-makers, Buck Rogers and Flash Gordon appearing in print and on screen to envision a future no one believed could become reality within their lifetime. International symbols of a future world, they provided a ready supply of material, establishing a backdrop to isolated pockets of serious research. However, from September 1944, when the Germans began launching several thousand V-2 rockets against Antwerp and London, the future seemed not quite so far away.

A key player in the development of the V-2 rocket, Wernher von Braun was brought to the United States after the war and began to give shape to a programme involving a wide range of ballistic rockets and missiles for which the US Army provided money and facilities. For a few years von Braun and his team worked with an increasing number of Army engineers and scientists to develop better versions of the V-2, a missile with a range of 200 miles (322km), and new versions capable of supporting battlefield troops.

By today's standards these were simple devices with limited range, but they ushered in a state of mind: that long-range rocketry, even missiles capable of crossing continents, might one day be possible. Although for the first decade after the end of the war this seemed far from realization, engineers and scientists worked to improve the state of the art and bring forward the age of "push-button" warfare. With several technical breakthroughs, the idea of an intercontinental ballistic missile (ICBM) became feasible by the mid-1950s, and work began on the United States' first rockets in this class – Atlas and Titan.

But the Soviets too sought the high ground of military superiority, resurrecting a solid body of research and engineering to do with rocketry which they had pursued from the 1930s onwards. Only with the great Stalin purges of 1936–38 had this work temporarily stopped, to be openly pursued again after the war ended in 1945. Stimulated by the German V-2, the Soviets pursued their own independent rocket designs and worked quickly to combine these projects with nuclear weapons, which they acquired in 1949. Encircled by US allies, the Soviet Union found that ICBMs offered the only realistic means of attacking the United States, and thus placed priority on very-long-range missiles.

It was this technology that gave the Soviet Union the means to put the first satellite in orbit in October 1957, but nobody, not even the Soviets, had imagined the panic it would cause as the West became fearful that the Soviet Union could apparently strike any city on Earth with atomic weapons. In reality the threat was minimal because the early missiles took several hours to prepare for flight and could conceivably be destroyed on the ground by US bombers, albeit with heavy losses to the attacking side. But the nuances were

Above: *From the 1930s onwards, the awareness that rocket flight might be possible in the near future informed a wide range of comics and science fiction novels, attracting readers such as this young soldier trapped in the Warsaw uprising in 1944 and reading a Flash Gordon novel!*

Opposite: *Rockets provide the means to propel objects into space because they carry fuel and oxidizer in separate tanks, unlike jet engines, which also combust fuel but take in air at the front. The first flight of a liquid propellant rocket was made by the American physics professor Dr Robert Goddard, here seen with the rocket supported in its A-frame from which it was launched on 16 March 1926.*

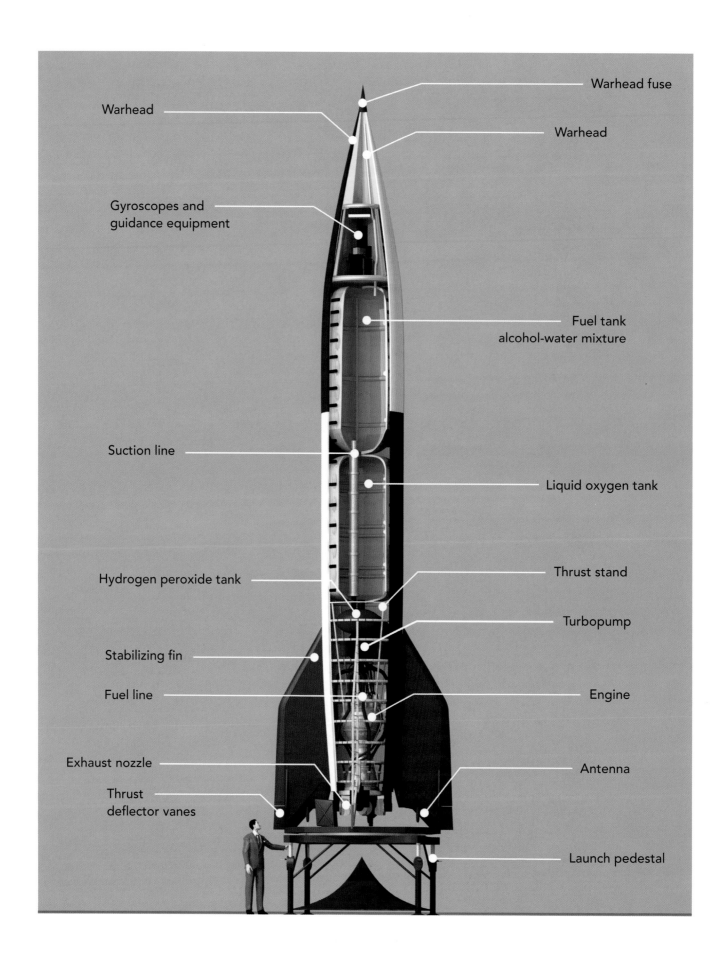

Warhead fuse

Warhead

Warhead

Gyroscopes and guidance equipment

Fuel tank alcohol-water mixture

Suction line

Liquid oxygen tank

Hydrogen peroxide tank

Thrust stand

Turbopump

Stabilizing fin

Fuel line

Engine

Exhaust nozzle

Antenna

Thrust deflector vanes

Launch pedestal

irrelevant: the fact that the Soviet Union was forging ahead with scientific and military superiority was the only message received by a general public weaned on US superiority during the Second World War.

CHALLENGE

Sputnik 1 had been one of the Soviet Union's contributions to the International Geophysical Year, extended to 18 months as a global effort at better understanding of the physical characteristics of Earth through scientific investigations. Launched since the late 1940s, so-called "sounding rockets" capable of shooting experiment packages to the edge of space seemed a fitting prelude to orbiting satellites that could remain in orbit just above the atmosphere, for years if necessary.

The Americans had their Vanguard programme proceeding without haste, but it was eclipsed by Sputnik. Reacting with shock to a failed Vanguard attempt three days after the Soviets put the dog Laika in space, von Braun's Army rocket team were pressed to send a satellite up as fast as possible and succeeded on 31 January 1958. But the shock of the Soviet Union's accomplishments forced plans for a dedicated US government agency to put the United States back on top, and NASA was formed in October.

However, the shocks kept on coming. Exactly two years to the day after Sputnik 1, the Soviets launched Luna 3, the first spacecraft to take pictures of the far side of the Moon – the opposite side to that continuously facing the Earth. Little more than three weeks earlier they had sent Luna 2 to an impact with its surface, the first man-made object to strike another world in space. As the achievements mounted up, the fear that the Soviet Union was on a runaway race leaving the Americans at the starting grid influenced the 1960 elections for US President. And thus began a domino sequence of events that turned the Space Race into a Moon Race.

The incumbent, President Eisenhower, had been constrained in his reaction to the Sputnik flights, supporting the one-man Mercury programme that sought to put the first human in space but not approving more advanced manned programmes. In contesting the election, Kennedy criticized the lack of pace,

Opposite: *The V-2 embodied every aspect of rocket design as it would evolve after the war, with graphite vanes in the exhaust operating like rudders in a ship's wake to keep it on course through tiny movements commanded by gyroscopes. This design would spur development of military missiles after the von Braun team was taken to America in 1945.*

Left: *A full-size model of the six Vostok spacecraft used to put Russia's first cosmonauts in orbit between 1961 and 1963, among whom was the first woman in space, Valentina Tereshkova. The light-coloured cylindrical section to the left is the second stage of the R-7 derivative used to lift it into orbit; forward of this is the spacecraft's instrument unit, to which is attached, at extreme right, the pressurised cabin which would bring the cosmonaut safely back to Earth.*

blaming Eisenhower for the lack of US successes and receiving some support within NASA for what a core of scientists and engineers felt was a lack of vision and an absence of urgency. Within this group, some had studied the possibility of flying to the Moon as a national goal, even creating preliminary designs of the kind of spacecraft that might achieve this and naming it Apollo. Yet despite the rising tide of criticism, Eisenhower held firm, refusing to approve funding for studies into Apollo and how it might provide for three men to fly around the Moon, perhaps by the end of the 1960s, and prepare the way for a landing on the surface sometime during the 1970s. These matters influenced the American people and played a small part in putting Kennedy into the White House, a president openly committed to "make America great again".

For all that, within the first few weeks of assuming office in January 1961, Kennedy displayed little real enthusiasm for space, only marginally increasing funds for von Braun's big rockets, called Saturn, which were being prepared for imminent flight. They were the first big rockets designed and built anywhere purely for launching large payloads into orbit, rather than missiles designed to send warheads to intercontinental destinations. Nonetheless, in the first quarter of Kennedy's presidency, the only US-funded manned spacecraft – the tiny one-man Mercury capsule – was moving towards placing the first human in space.

Then, on 12 April, the Soviet Union's Yuri Gagarin stole that trophy, causing the United States another shock. Just as Sputnik had led to the formation of NASA, so would this single flight send reverberations to the very top of the US political pyramid. A mere five days later, another propaganda disaster followed when a CIA-backed invasion of Cuba in an attempt to oust its Communist-revolutionary prime minister, Fidel Castro, floundered and the United States suffered a humiliating defeat in the race to impress undecided nations in the developing world. Turning to Vice President Lyndon B. Johnson, Kennedy demanded a plan to beat the Soviets at their own game, out there in space, asking if the United States should build a big space station, race to the Moon or head for Mars! The experts who had supported the shelved Apollo programme convinced Johnson that a Moon landing was achievable and probably could take place slightly earlier than the Soviets would manage. And that recommendation led Kennedy to take a drive from the White House to deliver the message on "Urgent National Needs" to the Joint Session of Congress on 25 May.

Left: *An iconic reminder of the former glory days of the Soviet space programme, the world's first spaceman – Yuri Gagarin – is remembered in numerous statues, such as this one erected in Moscow.*

Opposite: *The Soviet Union's Semyorka R-7 ballistic missile formed the basis for Sputnik 1 and for the Vostok launches that carried Yuri Gagarin into orbit, but had a thrust more than twice that of the biggest rocket being built in the United States, the Titan ICBM.*

Left: *In recent years, Russia has seized upon the success of space engineers, technicians and scientists of the Soviet Union to encourage young people into technical and mathematical subjects. Moscow has revamped its exhibition on space pioneers and reopened its hall of fame to reflect these successes.*

THE LUNAR EFFECT

It is said by those for whom the Moon, the Sun, the stars and the planets hold a special connection with their lives that the heavens are linked directly to human beings and that we have only to open our minds and be particularly aware of our sensitivities to know the strength of that connection.

Scientific explanations have come to play a pivotal role in judging the reliability or otherwise of facts and figures that bombard daily life with rationality and proof. Yet science can only describe what it can measure, weigh or interpret; it cannot explain the reason for anything, only point to what it knows to describe it. And because there is so much we have yet to discover, it is wise to remember that dogmatism is the enemy of discovery.

It must have been difficult for dispersed groups of primitive people around the world to understand the heavens, living unaware of other communities and geographically as far apart as Europe and Mesoamerica. Yet across the world, and down the ages from Neolithic times, humans have sought to represent the heavens and the lights they see in the sky through art and pictures: art that shows the Moon and the stars in paintings and on cave walls; sculptures in bone and rock that appear to show, in clear and purposeful marks, the passage of time as measured by the movement of the Sun and the Moon.

Great monuments, Stonehenge among them, testify to humankind's preoccupation with the Sun and the Moon. Whatever purpose the huge

Opposite: *Merging his characters into the colours of the landscape, the German Romantic painter Caspar David Friedrich imagines watchers gazing at the Moon as ships venture towards the horizon, an unwitting foretaste of the "new ocean of space" imagined by a speechwriter for President Kennedy.*

Below: *Raised in a part of England settled permanently for the past 10,000 years, Stonehenge represents an association with cultural identities which many believe connected the female menstrual cycle and the marking of the seasons with the cyclical motion of the Moon back and forth along the horizon.*

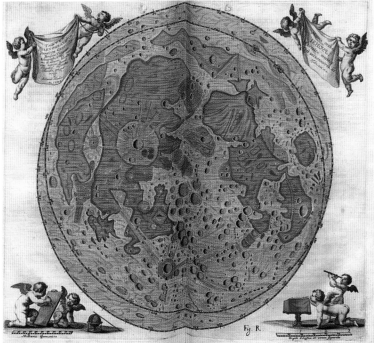

stone edifice had as it evolved through several hundred years of modification, 2,500 years before Roman armies landed on the shores of the British Isles, it remains enigmatic. Yet most of the alignments, if genuinely intended, point to the Sun and the Moon, and debate persists over which had precedence over the other in the eyes of its builders.

Left: *Hailed by some as the "father of lunar topography", the 17th-century mayor of Gdansk and astronomer Johannes Hevelius drew this map of the Moon's principle features in 1645. He was the first of many generations of lunar mapmakers before the robotic precursors of human exploration 320 years later paved the way for Apollo.*

CHAPTER 2

THE MEANS TO GO

Two technologies were required to reach the Moon: rocket power to propel the spacecraft to escape velocity and on to a translunar flight path; and the vehicles to take the astronauts to the surface. The size and power of the rockets required would be determined by the method chosen to reach the Moon, while the spacecraft would be kept as small and as light in weight as possible to match the finite capabilities of the rockets chosen to send them on their way. Overall, the method chosen to reach the Moon would have to be within the capabilities of the available rockets.

Right: *The heavy lifting power to get to the Moon would require a rocket so big that it would dwarf anything designed when the first satellites were launched. A development test version of that rocket, Saturn V AS-500F, makes its way to the launch pad on 25 May 1966, five years to the day after President Kennedy announced the goal.*

FROM JUPITER TO SATURN

Key to achieving an inventory of bigger space launchers was the experienced team of rocket scientists and engineers working for the US Army at Huntsville, Alabama. Formed around a nucleus of German V-2 personnel, the Army Ballistic Missile Agency's Development Operations Division grew in size and capacity, producing early rockets and missiles for the military until it was transferred to NASA in 1960. Renamed the Marshall Space Flight Center, it had Wernher von Braun as its director, in charge of the entire facility.

During the early 1950s, while working at Fort Bliss, Texas before moving to Huntsville, von Braun's team had been responsible for the Redstone rocket. In several respects this was little more than a completely redesigned V-2 with a range of up to 200 miles (322km). First flown in August 1953, early models suffered the usual spate of catastrophes prevalent among rockets and missiles of the time, but the reliability gradually increased and Redstone entered service with the Army in 1958. Early variants used a mixture of ethyl alcohol mixed with water as a fuel, with liquid oxygen as the oxidizer. Later Redstones used an exotic fuel mixture known as Hydyne and this increased performance.

Redstone was followed by Jupiter, a missile developed to throw a nuclear warhead across a distance of 1,490 miles (2,400km), providing the Army with its first medium-range ballistic missile and a demonstrated accuracy placing 50 per cent of tested rounds within ½ mile (800m) of their target. Powered by a single Rocketdyne S-3 motor delivering a thrust of 150,000lb (667.2kN) from a combination of kerosene and liquid oxygen, Jupiter was first launched in March 1957 from Cape Canaveral.

For aficionados, the name "Jupiter" for a missile can mean several other rockets. For instance, Jupiter-A was actually a series of Redstone missile tests during development of the various systems required for the Jupiter medium-range missile. And Jupiter-C was actually a version of the Redstone, developed from the Jupiter-A configuration, which had solid propellant upper stages, each a series of drum-shaped barrels inside one another, which fired in sequence. It was a rocket of this type which placed America's first satellite in orbit (Explorer 1).

Use of further Jupiter-C rockets for launching satellites prompted the name Juno I, with satellite-launching versions of the Jupiter medium-range missile known as Juno II. But Juno I could lift a weight of only 24lb (11kg) into orbit and, of the six attempts to launch satellites, all during 1958, only three were successful.

SATURN IS GO!

The turning point for work being done by the Army Ballistic Missile Agency came on 26 November 1956, when the Department of Defense decreed that only the Air Force and Navy could develop and operate missiles with a range greater than 200 miles (322km). In an effort to avoid duplication, the Air Force took over operational deployment of the medium-range Jupiter missile.

But the satellite launcher that von Braun was tasked with developing was a fast-track approach to achieve heavyweight status for launching big payloads into space and, as it turned out, would prove critical in putting men on the Moon. That work began in 1956, when the Army sought to acquire a capacity for placing 9–18-tonne satellites in orbit. Calculations showed that a rocket with a first-stage thrust of 1.5 million lb (6,672kN) would be required, 50 per cent more powerful than anything the Soviets had launched.

Opposite: *A decade before Sputnik, Wernher von Braun developed the Redstone missile, here seen before its first flight in May 1953. This, and the subsequent Jupiter missile, would provide the tooling to build the Saturn I, the United States' first big space-launch system.*

Below: *Designated PGM-19A, the Jupiter missile came off the drawing boards of the Army Ballistic Missile Agency Development Operations Division run by Wernher von Braun. Although it did not achieve fame as a military weapon, it served as a space-launch vehicle and led to the Saturn I.*

WERNHER VON BRAUN (1912–77)

Born to nobility in Wirsitz, Germany, von Braun was entitled to use the title Baron (von), a categorization abolished after World War I, with the right to retain it as part of the family name. His mother was related to several European sovereigns of the Middle Ages, including Philip III of France, Robert III of Scotland and Edward III of England, his father Magnus being a civil servant and politician.

The young Wernher developed a passion for astronomy. Inspired by the exploits of Fritz von Opel and Max Valier, who experimented with rocket motors in record-breaking cars, he was arrested at the age of 12 after creating chaos by sending toy wagons down the street propelled by fireworks tied to the back! Excelling in science and mathematics, he attended the technical college in Berlin and joined the *Verein für Raumschiffarht* (German Society for Space

Travel) which had been set up by enthusiasts and a few serious experimenters.

When the Nazi Party came to power in 1933, von Braun was working on his doctorate, which was awarded on 27 July 1934 for work on combustion tests, classified by the German Army since it defined the principles by which large liquid propellant rocket motors could be developed. Although Robert Goddard had launched the first liquid propellant rocket in 1926, none of the work done by von Braun was influenced by this or later activity as developed by the American scientist.

The Nazi government closed down all private rocket societies, and von Braun accepted an offer from Major Walter Dornberger to work for the army and pull together a team to build a ballistic missile. After several years' work, the test site at Peenemünde on Germany's Baltic coast provided a home for what became an enormous effort to produce the V-2 rocket, with a range of 200 miles (370km). Operational use of the V-2 began in September 1944 against London and Antwerp. Of the 5,200 produced, approximately 3,172 were launched, killing about 4,500 people and injuring a further 11,000.

Von Braun and a small nucleus of the rocket team surrendered to the Americans at the end of the war and were taken to the United States to work on ballistic missiles and rockets for the US Army. Von Braun bv ecame head of the Marshall Space Flight Center when the Army facility at Huntsville, Alabama, was taken over by NASA and renamed, his most notable success being management of the Saturn I and Saturn V rockets, which were pivotal in taking men to the Moon. After a brief period at NASA headquarters, von Braun left NASA in 1972 and joined industry, but died of pancreatic cancer five years later.

Left: *Uncharacteristically bearded, Wernher von Braun developed the Saturn series rockets, seen here as the four from right in the photograph, the largest of which is the Saturn V.*

Opposite: *Von Braun, with his arm in plaster as the result of a car accident, after his surrender to the Americans at the end of World War II in 1945.*

To put this in perspective, the Atlas ICBM had a thrust of 360,000lb (1,600kN) although it was yet to fly, while the Titan had a thrust of 430,000lb (1,913kN). When utilized as satellite launchers, these rockets could place payloads in orbit weighing 1 tonne and 3.5 tonnes respectively – very far short of what was being envisaged. Nevertheless, the team proposed Juno III and Juno IV concepts. But they also looked at a more ambitious idea, designated Juno V.

The idea around Juno V was to cluster eight Redstone stage tanks around a single central Jupiter stage, with propulsion provided by four Rocketdyne E-1 engines, each delivering a thrust of up to 380,000lb (1,690kN) for a total lift-off thrust of 1.52 million lb (6,761kN). The E-1 was only a design concept and had not been built. Von Braun's team opted for eight H-1 engines instead, each delivering a thrust of 188,000lb (836kN) for the total required lift-off thrust. The H-1 was a re-engineered simplification of the S-3 originally developed for the Redstone. Rocketdyne was given a contract to develop the H-1 in September 1958, by which date the Juno V was being referred to as Saturn, a name formally adopted five months later.

Through a series of convoluted paths, the Saturn I rocket, as it was named, was to be developed in two versions: Block I with only the first stage for

Opposite: *An early model of the Atlas ICBM is readied for flight in January 1959, soon to be deployed as the United States' first missile capable of firing nuclear warheads to the Soviet Union from bases in the United States.*

Below: *The mighty Titan rocket lifts off on a test flight. More powerful than Atlas, both missiles would be adapted for the space programme, and each would send astronauts into space in the run-up to Apollo missions.*

ballistic flights, to verify that it was possible to launch a clustered rocket; and Block II with an S-IV upper stage powered by six RL-10 engines each with a thrust of 15,000lb (66.72kN) consuming liquid hydrogen, kept at -423°F (-252.87°C), and liquid oxygen, stored below -298°F (-183°C).

The first four Saturn I launch vehicles were single-stage flights employing early models of the H-1 which had a thrust of 165,000lb (733.9kN), falling short of the desired total lift-off thrust until the developed H-1 was available for the last six flights. The first flight with an S-IV was on 29 January 1964, the fifth flight of a Saturn I and the first rocket of this type to deliver a payload into orbit. The last Saturn I with a cryogenic S-IV stage was launched on 30 July 1965, by which time a very much larger Saturn rocket had emerged.

During the latter part of 1961, von Braun's team proposed a C-5 with five F-1 engines in the first stage to create a massive rocket with the height of a 36-storey building and weighing as much as a Navy warship. Very soon known simply as Saturn V, it would be capable of placing 100 tonnes into Earth orbit or sending 45 tonnes to the Moon, and this was the way NASA would send its astronauts to the lunar surface.

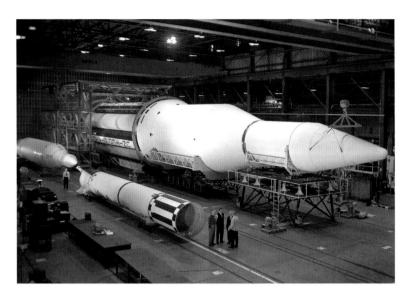

Above: *Given scale by the Redstone rocket (foreground) and Jupiter missile (left), the enormous Saturn I employed clustered tanks fabricated from the same tooling and offered a quick solution to acquiring a heavy-lift launcher.*

Opposite: *The first of ten Saturn I rockets lifts off from Cape Canaveral on 27 October 1961, heralding the start of the United States' winning streak over the Soviet Union in the race to the Moon.*

Below: *The clustered Redstone and Jupiter tanks for the Saturn I were secured together by a spider-beam at the forward end and a thrust structure at the rear, which supported eight H-1 rocket motors to provide a lift-off thrust greatly in excess of the Soviet Union's R-7 rocket.*

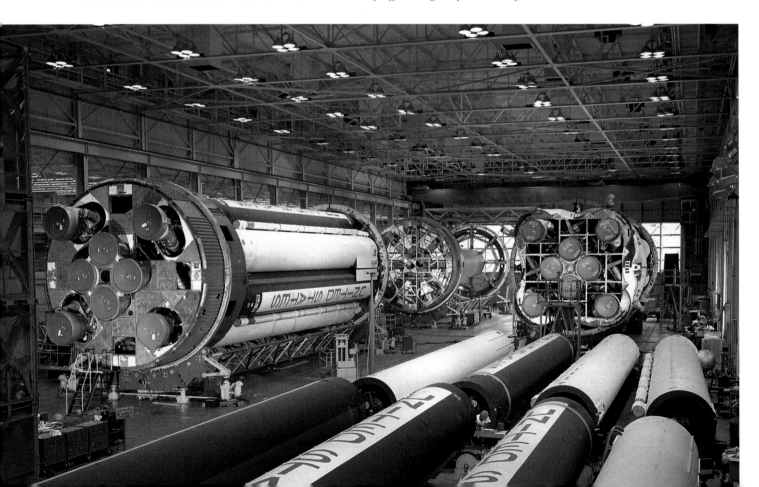

HOW ROCKETS WORK

Like jet engines, rockets are reaction devices that operate by burning a fuel with an oxidizer, known as propellant, to create energy which is used to do work – an action that causes a reaction. A jet engine takes in air from the atmosphere, which is 21 per cent oxygen, the gas which allows combustion of the fuel, while a rocket carries its own oxygen in a tank and can therefore work in the vacuum of space. The jet relies on taking in air while the rocket is entirely self-contained. There are two types of rocket motor: solid propellant and liquid propellant.

A solid propellant rocket combines both oxidizer and fuel mixed in a solid form, while the liquid propellant rocket motor operates by bringing the two propellants together in a combustion chamber. When operating, both solid and liquid motors burn their propellants to produce gases which expand in pressure and are released through a nozzle. It is the velocity of the gases leaving the nozzle which produces thrust. The reaction to this thrust (the action) causes the rocket, or missile, to move in the opposite direction (reaction).

A common fallacy is to believe that the exhausted gases push against air to propel the device in the opposite direction, but this is completely false. In fact, rocket motors of any type only achieve their optimum performance when operating in a vacuum. This is because there is no atmospheric pressure pushing against the nozzle to reduce the exhaust velocity and there is no pressure pushing on the nose of the rocket or missile to prevent it achieving maximum velocity.

Different combinations of propellant produce different levels of efficiency in the rocket motor. The basic measure of propellant performance is known as specific impulse, which at its most basic means the amount of thrust that can be achieved per kg of propellant burned for one second: the higher the specific impulse, the greater the efficiency of the rocket. A propellant combination such as kerosene and liquid oxygen is about 300 seconds; using liquid hydrogen as a fuel, the specific impulse can be up to 435 seconds.

Below: *Liquid propellant motors work by delivering fuel and oxidizer to a combustion chamber where the mixture ignites to produce an exhaust as an action, the forward motion of the rocket being an equal and opposite reaction.*

To achieve this the propellants, fuel and the necessary oxidizer to achieve combustion, are delivered to the combustion chamber by turbopumps, which are themselves powered either by very small quantities of those propellants siphoned off to form a workable energy from a small combustion chamber to drive the pumps, or a separate store of propellants. The propellants are delivered to the main combustion chamber through a spray system rather like a shower head, where concentric rings are separately connected via tubes that in turn are connected to the main delivery lines. The "throat" is where the combusted liquids turned to gas achieve tremendous pressure and are accelerated – exactly like air being released from the neck of a balloon to propel it in the opposite direction to the line of thrust.

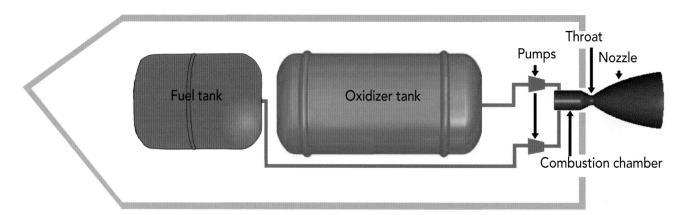

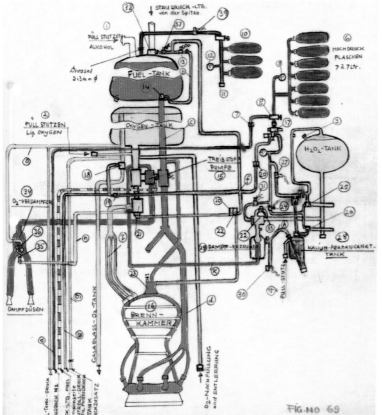

Above: *The core stage and four rocket boosters for the Soyuz launch vehicle which forms the workhorse for Russia's space programme today. Developed from the R-7 ballistic missile of the late 1950s, it has served first the Soviet Union and latterly Russia well as the main launch vehicle for satellites, spacecraft and manned missions to space stations in Earth orbit.*

Left: *A technical drawing of the V-2 rocket engine as dissected and scrutinized by British engineers after World War II. In this view, propellants are fed from separate tanks by a turbopump driven by a hydrogen peroxide chamber (right) and burned in the combustion chamber to expend and generate gases which produce thrust.*

CHAPTER 3

PREPARING THE WAY

When the decision to build the mighty Saturn V was announced on 20 January 1962, the space agency still did not know how it would reach the Moon. There were three possible methods, each with its own flaws and advantages.

The simplest and most obvious would be to build a giant rocket to send a spacecraft direct to the Moon. On approach it would turn around, fire a retro-rocket and land using legs deployed prior to touchdown. After some time at the surface, during which the crew would get out and retrieve samples, the upper section of the spacecraft would fire a separate rocket motor to blast off and head straight back to Earth. Known as Direct Ascent (DA), this process would call for a rocket of such immense proportions that there were serious technical challenges to its timely development. Moreover, it would not

Opposite: *Options for Moon landing modes were made possible by the development of the powerful F-1 rocket motor, five of which would be installed in the first stage of the Saturn V, giving it a payload capability many times that of the largest Soviet launch vehicle. Standing by the rocket, von Braun provides a sense of scale.*

Left: *Production of the F-1 at Rocketdyne's manufacturing facility at Canoga Park, California, where the world's most powerful rocket motor would be built and tested before delivery to NASA's Michoud Assembly Facility for installation in the first stage fabricated by Boeing. The entire stage would then be test-fired on the ground at the Mississippi Test Facility before delivery to Cape Canaveral.*

allow an opportunity for reconnaissance of particular areas so that an informed decision could be made about preferred landing sites. However, it would allow a landing to be achieved from a single launch, which was an advantage not shared by the alternative.

Known as Earth Orbit Rendezvous (EOR), the second option required the launch of many smaller Saturn rockets to assemble in Earth's orbit a spacecraft similar to that of the Direct Ascent approach. After completion, and fuelled

Right: *Demonstrating the layout of a typical rocket motor, the F-1 incorporated a combustion chamber where liquid oxygen was mixed with an RP-1 fuel, a refined kerosene, to generate a thrust of 1.5 million lb (6,672kN).*

Below: *Similar to a shower head, but taking in liquid oxygen (green) and RP-1 fuel (red) instead of water, the F-1 injector manifold sat on top of the combustion chamber where the propellants were mixed, producing a temperature of up to 5,800°F (3,200°C). Exhaust gases were directed out the nozzle, formally known as the expansion skirt.*

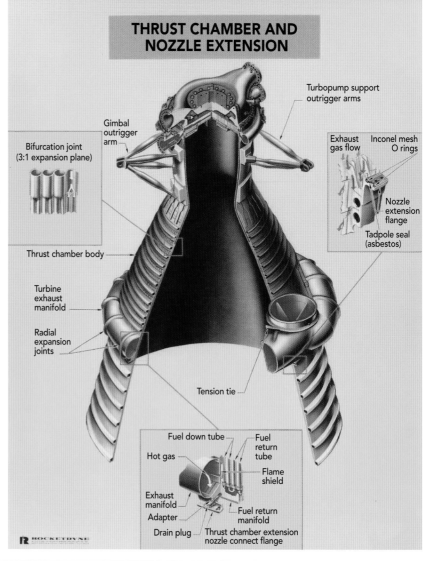

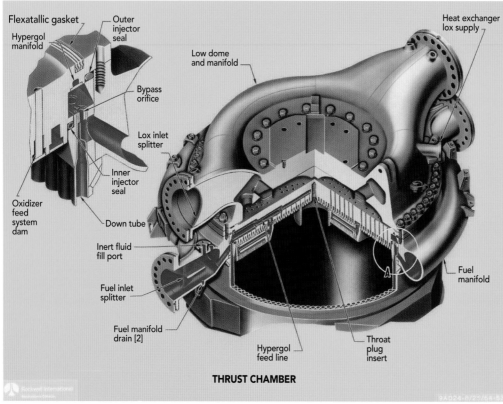

THRUST CHAMBER

Opposite: *The first stage of a Saturn V in the giant vehicle assembly building at the Kennedy Space Center. Here, the S-IC stage would be mated with the S-II second stage and the S-IVB third stage before the spacecraft itself was attached to the top, creating a structure 36 storeys tall.*

THE KENNEDY PARADOX

As 35th President of the United States, John F. Kennedy presided over some of the most momentous events of the 20th century, including the challenge of sending humans to the Moon. Aided by gifted speechwriters, appealing to the awe engendered by the proclamation of outstanding goals, Kennedy would assert: "We set sail on this new sea because there is new knowledge to be gained, and new rights to be won, and they must be won and used for the progress of all people. For space science, like nuclear science and all technology, has no conscience of its own."

Yet for all his rhetorical fervour, the youthful president had little interest in space research, or in building a technological base constructed around its achievements. Generally credited with having begun the expansion of the space programme from which it would never turn back, Kennedy had in fact attempted to reverse his decision on several occasions before his assassination on 22 November 1963. Having never wanted to select the Moon goal in the first place, he sought an alternative that would be a more lasting response to Soviet space achievements. But he had struggled to find alternatives as bold or as galvanizing for his national audience.

In debating options with a select gathering of government leaders in the White House before deciding on the Moon goal in late April 1961, Kennedy argued fiercely – as revealed by tape-recorded conversations – appealing for some other great national project to mobilize the nation and garner support from uncommitted countries around the world. Only when David Bell, director of the Bureau of the Budget, argued that the Moon programme would bring employment did the President begin to converge on the consensus among that small group: that nothing short of a dramatic space achievement would undermine Soviet propaganda.

Below: *Despite claims that President Kennedy was a devout supporter of an expanded US space programme, his Moon decision was an opportunistic attempt to use NASA for political purposes. Within 18 months he was desperately seeking ways to overturn that allegiance. His assassination prevented that, but galvanized NASA into an even deeper commitment.*

by other rockets, the entire apparatus would fire out of orbit, travel to the Moon and carry out a sequence close to that for the Direct Ascent method. While conservative in approach and incorporating sequential steps to allow a safe abort during the build-up phase, it would be very costly on rockets and associated launches, each expedition taking a long time to mount.

When President Kennedy was persuaded by senior NASA managers that a Moon landing within the 1960s was feasible, the Direct Ascent mode was the favoured approach. There were concerns about the process of rendezvous and docking of two or more vehicles in space. Nobody had attempted anything like that, and to add a level of uncertainty could imperil the whole programme and send NASA down a path of insoluble problems. But there was a third way.

Throughout 1960 and 1961, a small group of engineers led by John C. Houbolt at NASA's Langley Research Center, in Virginia, proposed the Lunar Orbit Rendezvous (LOR) mission mode. It involved the use of a single Saturn V to send two spacecraft to the Moon – one to remain in lunar orbit and act as a mother ship and one to go down to the surface. After a suitable stay, the upper half of the Moon ship would use the landing stage as a launch platform and take the crew back to the mother ship, which would then return to Earth.

BATTLEGROUNDS

The three competing modes were vigorously fought over between respective advocates. Not least of these was the prime contractor for the Apollo spacecraft – North American Aviation (NAA) – which been selected on 28 November 1961 to build the vehicle that, at the time, everyone believed would land on the Moon, whether Direct Ascent or EOR was selected. The company's advertising agency enthusiastically set to work on promotions in the trade press, on billboards and in media interviews, along with an employee recruitment drive. (Although Apollo design concepts had been underway since mid-1960, the Eisenhower administration had refused to release funds to take the next step towards its development, so the concept had languished on the shelf until taken down by advocates shifting Kennedy towards his announcement.) Now, the addition of the LOR option, which threatened to strip NAA of its proud role by having another spacecraft actually land, was only the start of a series of vicious recriminations which almost toppled the entire venture.

To support the management of NASA's expanding human space flight programme, the Manned Spacecraft Center (MSC) was to be built on a site outside Houston, Texas. But there were fierce opponents who kept the debate boiling for several months. Finally, on

Below: *When Apollo was first proposed in 1960, the assumption was that it would eventually be adapted to land on the Moon, using a descent stage with lags to stabilize it after touchdown, as shown in this model.*

Above: *Eventually converting everyone to his Lunar Orbit Rendezvous (LOR) mode, John Houbolt faced down opposition and ridicule when he refused to give up on the idea of using a smaller lander to separate from the Apollo mother ship in lunar orbit and descend to the surface.*

7 June 1962, von Braun gave his official approval and it appeared that the decision for LOR was inevitable. However, this was not so.

A staunch opponent of the entire Apollo Moon programme was Kennedy's chief science adviser, Jerome B. Wiesner, who fiercely opposed the LOR mode. During September 1962, Wiesner openly opposed the decision in front of journalists while the President was being shown around the Marshall Space Flight Center by von Braun. Wiesner was not only an opponent of the Moon programme, he was opposed to human space flight in any form, believing it to be wasteful and unnecessary, and had told Kennedy so in pre-election briefings. Unknown to many close advisers, these negative thoughts began to work away at Kennedy, but the public outburst was an embarrassment on this feel-good occasion when the media too were being given sight of the emerging programme.

Seeds of discontent sown by Wiesner began to influence senior NASA

Left: *Dr Kurt Deus, who came to the United States after World War II to work for the US Army and eventually for NASA, was promoted to be in charge of NASA's Kennedy Space Center, where he oversaw the completion of Saturn V facilities supporting Moon missions.*

management, especially when he tasked Nicholas E. Golovin, a former NASA engineer, to make his own analysis. This destabilized the timeline for a few weeks and it was only on 11 July 1962 that a formal announcement was made about the LOR decision. Nor was this the end of the matter. Wiesner attempted to find time with the President so that he could try to change his mind and begin to reverse the decision. By the time he was assigned a slot in the President's diary, however, Kennedy was in the midst of the Cuban Missile Crisis and Wiesner thought better of it.

Had it not been for the failed Bay of Pigs invasion (the CIA-sponsored coup attempt in Cuba), coupled with the flight of Yuri Gagarin, Kennedy would never have been nudged into the Moon decision in May 1961; and had it not been for the crisis with Soviet premier Khrushchev in October 1962, it is possible that he would have been swayed by Wiesner and begun the process to cancel Apollo there and then. There was a reason for this: Kennedy had always measured success over the Soviets on rocket power alone; the first Saturn I flight on 27 October 1961 had equalled the Soviets on thrust alone, and to Kennedy the race had already been won.

Increasingly over the last 18 months of his life, from mid-1962 onwards, Kennedy sought ways to extricate himself from the Moon goal, even putting out an offer to the Soviets to "go to the Moon together". Internally, the White House was at loggerheads with NASA boss Jim Webb over the way Apollo was being used to expand a wide range of potentially beneficial applications including communications, navigation, environmental research, astronomical science and planetary explanation. On this, Oval Office tapes show an aggressive Kennedy talking down Webb and demanding that everything must be subservient to the Moon goal – another example of the paradoxical figure who occupied the White House.

We now know that the Soviets did not formally begin their own programme for sending cosmonauts to the Moon until 1964, the year after Kennedy's assassination. It is clear from archives that the Soviets never believed the Americans were serious about the Moon goal and doubted that it could be done in the time laid down. Only when the commitment was given greater impetus under President Johnson did they mobilize a programme of their own.

Below: *NASA Administrator James E. Webb, the man promoted by President Kennedy to head the nation's civilian space programme between the beginning of 1961 and the end of 1968. Webb presided over the biggest expansion of NASA in its history, managing the agency during the years of Apollo.*

Above: *The soaring budget for NASA, doubling each year between 1961 and 1965, led to a major expansion of launch pads and facilities (seen here in 1964) supporting both civilian and military launches, the majority conducted by the Air Force.*

SPACESHIPS GALORE

When the Moon goal was declared in 1961, astronauts with space flight experience were few and far between. At NASA there was only Alan Shepard, who had made a 15-minute ballistic hop on 5 May from a launch pad at Cape Canaveral to a splashdown off the coast of Florida. This was 20 days before Kennedy's historic announcement and almost a month after Yuri Gagarin orbited the Earth.

A second test shot carried "Gus" Grissom on another ballistic flight two months after Shepard, followed by the first American manned orbital flight when John Glenn circled the Earth three times on 20 February 1962. Three more Mercury orbital flights took place on 24 May (Malcolm Scott Carpenter), 3 October (Walter M. Schirra) and 15 May 1963 (Gordon Cooper).

The tiny Mercury capsule was only just big enough for one astronaut and had been designed for a maximum flight duration of 24 hours, although the last mission had been stretched to 34 hours through a series of modifications and upgrades. With the Moon goal set and flights expected to begin around

Below: *By 1963 NASA was managing four manned space vehicles: Mercury (bottom right), Gemini (centre right) and Apollo and the Lunar Module (top right). Their three launch systems are lined up on the far left of the picture: Mercury Atlas (right), Gemini-Titan (centre) and Saturn V (left), increasing in size with each generation from one- to three-man vehicles.*

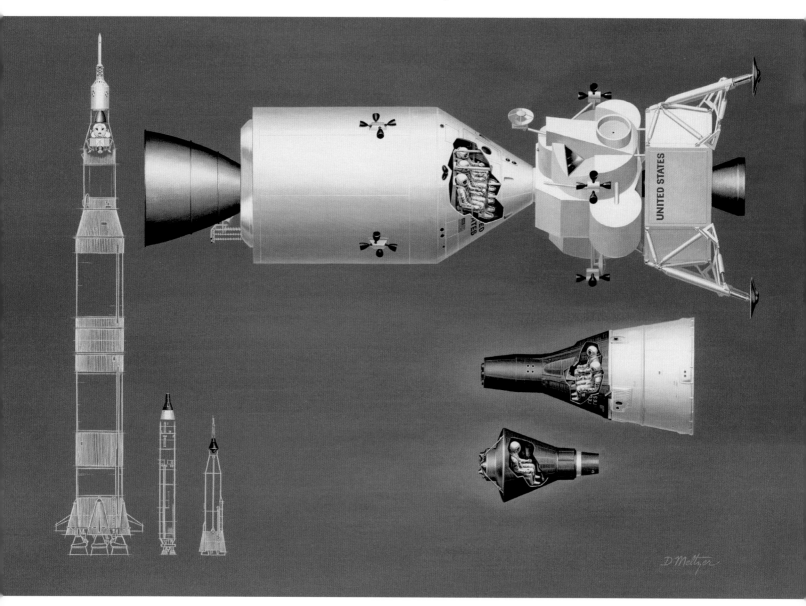

1965, NASA began the Gemini programme in late 1961, a two-man successor to Mercury designed to provide astronauts with interim flight experience for Apollo before the Moon-bound mother ship was ready.

Gemini was vital for gaining experience with the techniques of orbital rendezvous and docking, for which the "chase" vehicle would have to hunt down a "target" previously placed in a stable orbit of the Earth. Mercury could not manoeuvre in orbit, only rotate around its own axis, whereas Gemini had thrusters to enable it to change path and raise or lower its orbit and to move forwards or backwards in relation to another object close by. Once feared as a threat to the Earth Orbit Rendezvous mode, the Lunar Obit Rendezvous technique incorporated these capabilities which would be crucial to the success of the Moon landing.

The Gemini programme would also demonstrate spacewalking, or EVA (Extra-Vehicular Activity) in NASA parlance, to test life-support equipment and demonstrate the ability of astronauts to work outside their vehicles – another essential element in the catalogue of techniques and technologies untried and many not invented when the Moon decision was made. EVA in weightlessness would be a daunting challenge, as the Gemini programme would demonstrate.

A third capability, as yet untried but essential for the Moon mission, was long-duration flight. A Moon mission could last up to ten days, including three days each way, some rest time in lunar orbit and two days down on the

Above: *Pivotal to the success of Apollo, the two-man Gemini spacecraft demonstrated two-week flight duration, spacewalking and rendezvous and docking, manoeuvring itself in orbit and the hydrogen/oxygen fuel-cell concept for electrical power.*

Above and opposite: *Early concepts of the Lunar Module were very different to the vehicle actually built, as evidenced by this 1962 configuration.*

surface, conducting an EVA and returning to the Apollo mother ship. Gemini was designed to allow astronauts to remain in Earth's orbit for two weeks, with doctors evaluating their physiological state and observing any unexpected symptoms that might be consequences of weightlessness.

When the contract to build Gemini was awarded to the McDonnell Aircraft Company, the people who built the Mercury capsules, on 22 December 1961, NASA expected to begin flying astronauts aboard this two-man spacecraft in 1964. Under the plan, two unmanned test flights would precede ten manned missions, all flights to be launched by an adapted Titan II launch vehicle, more powerful than the Atlas rocket used to launch Mercury orbital missions. For rendezvous and docking flights, an Agena upper stage launched by an Atlas rocket would place itself in orbit as the target vehicle for the Gemini chase vehicle which would be sent up one orbit later.

During 1962 NASA authorized development of the giant Saturn V powered by five giant F-1 engines, and decided on the Lunar Orbit Rendezvous mode, from which flowed a request in July for bids to build the Lunar Module (LM), originally known as the Lunar Excursion Module. Following Apollo, Gemini and Saturn V, this was the fourth and last major hardware decision following

the Moon goal announcement, and the contract went to Grumman Aircraft on 7 November 1962. To Grumman would go the glory of building the spacecraft that would land humans on the Moon and bring them back to Apollo.

A CHANGE OF GEAR

By the end of 1962, with elements of existing programmes showing high cost overruns and schedules slipping, there was a deep concern that the Moon was growing more distant and that Kennedy's stated goal would never be achieved. By around mid-1963 the situation was so bad that NASA boss Jim Webb decided to look around for solutions – steps so drastic as to completely restructure the organization, weed out senior managers clearly not up to the job and support those at senior level who had been arguing for a more disciplined approach.

NASA had inherited a lot of highly competent scientists and engineers who had helped build the backbone of the US aerospace industry over several decades, working with companies across the country. But they had been a unique set of highly qualified, highly individualistic people who found it hard to fit into a rapidly expanding government organization that had little time for individuality and an avaricious appetite for performance, demanding exclusive commitment to their profession no matter what the cost.

Starting in August 1963, a significant management restructuring took place, with the former head of NASA's human space flight programme, D. Brainerd Holmes, replaced by the energetic, demanding and uncompromising George Mueller. With him came a new style, which upset a lot of people – and found favour with many more. Mueller was certainly committed, leaving a well-paid job in industry to work for a government salary on a programme that was in disarray.

With an uncompromising attitude, he instilled commitment above everything else, through his famous "Sunday morning quarterback" meetings at which his senior managers got together every weekend to avoid cutting into weekday activation times. Mueller also believed that this would secure a sense of purpose, at a time when Saturday mornings also had work commitments and annual holidays ran only to a single two-week period each year.

Needing to transform the upper layers of management, he began to introduce the levels of talent and delivery that would get NASA on track for an intensively active period of preparation, without which the entire challenge would have been impossible to accomplish. The first of those who came to NASA under Mueller's auspices was a titan of management efficiency: US Air Force General Samuel Phillips. A career officer, combat pilot from World War II, negotiating officer for deployment of Thor ballistic missiles to Britain and director of the Minuteman ICBM programme, Phillips had *performance* written all over him. Mueller brought him in to head up the Apollo programme.

With Phillips came 55 highly talented Air Force officers under Project 55, a cohort of skilled engineer-managers from glittering careers in the armed services who exuded success. Around 60 more came before the end of the year. Brig. Gen. David "Davy" Jones became Phillips's deputy, Col. C. Bolender the Apollo mission director and Col. E. O'Connor director of industrial operations. Col. Sam Yarchin was put in charge of the Saturn V office to which von Braun reported from the Marshall Space Flight Center, responsible for overall development production of the giant rocket. The various stages of the spacecraft were made by different companies, Boeing building the S-IC first stage, North American Aviation the S-II second stage and McDonnell Douglas the S-IVB third stage.

The S-IVB stage was an outgrowth of the cryogenic S-IV stage that gave the Saturn I its ability to place payloads in orbit. By increasing the size of the stage and equipping it with a single Rocketdyne J-2 engine of 200,000lb (889.6kN) thrust, it had more than twice the output of its predecessor and would give the Saturn V added potency. Moreover, it could be restarted in orbit – a requirement driven by the need for the Apollo and Lunar Module, docked together and still attached to the S-IVB stage, to first enter a waiting orbit while all systems were checked before firing up again and heading for the Moon. And in a cluster of five, the J-2 itself would power the cryogenic S-II second stage of Saturn V.

From the availability of the S-IVB came an opportunity to cut costs by eliminating unnecessary test flights. Mueller and Phillips had been

Below: *For some time NASA hoped to be able to bring two-man Gemini capsules back from space to touch down on dry land, rather than splash down in the Atlantic Ocean. To do this, a paraglider concept was studied, in which the capsule would deploy an inflatable wing after re-entry to conduct a controlled glide to the ground. It proved too difficult to implement, however.*

GEM BOXES

During 1963, as NASA's management structure was failing to keep pace with expected schedules and was seriously compromising the timeline for reaching the Moon by the end of 1969, Dr George E. Mueller of the high-tech company TRW became increasingly involved with the space agency. Accepting an offer from NASA boss Jim Webb to head up the office responsible for Mercury, Gemini and Apollo, on the basis that he could impose his own management techniques and completely reorganize the way it was run, Mueller made striking changes which ensured that NASA would reach the Moon by the end of the decade.

The 1960s were a time of radical change in the way major defence and technology projects were managed. With the Air Force responsible for directing large missile programmes on massive budgets, lessons from World War II introduced the concept of systems management; Mueller was a convert to that doctrine of highly structured, highly disciplined vertical management ladders where accountability and responsibility for actions were paramount.

Mueller became famous throughout NASA for his adoption of Program Evaluation and Review Technique (PERT) procedures for identifying and tracking the minutest part of a schedule incorporating several thousand line elements – an operational procedure that replaced the old "waterfall" charts where things simply flowed from one line to another without disclosing the consequential effect of a delay or a postponement in development, testing or qualification. Taking Mueller's initials, these were known as GEM boxes – because they held the jewels of success.

Left: *NASA manned flight boss George Mueller (spectacled), with Charles Mathews (far left), Wernher von Braun (second from left) and Sam Phillips (right) – chief architects of the 1963 revolution at NASA.*

concerned about the sequential approach to testing new rockets, the Saturn I being a classic case of sluggish development and slow maturation. Von Braun's team had carried forward their conservative approach, originating with the V-2 and extending through the Redstone and Jupiter programmes. The Huntsville team fired four Saturn I first-stage units on ballistic flights before adding the cryogenic S-IV and then testing that through several successive launches.

When Mueller came on board, von Braun had persuaded senior management to schedule four manned Apollo test flights on the Saturn I, beginning in late 1965 and concurrent with the second phase of the two-man Gemini programme. The idea was to test Apollo systems in Earth's orbit so that by the time the Saturn V came along, perhaps by 1967, the equipment and the astronauts would be ready for a fast-track race to the Moon. But the limited lifting capacity of the basic Saturn I meant that the Apollo spacecraft could carry only limited consumables and represent only a slimmed-down version of the definitive spacecraft.

Mueller and Phillips came up with a plan to eliminate the four Saturn I manned Apollo flights and put the more powerful S-IVB stage on the first stage of the Saturn I (redesignated as the Saturn IB), using that to test-fly a fully representative Apollo spacecraft in Earth's orbit. This would move Saturn IB/Apollo flights to beyond the Gemini programme, with those missions flown before fully fledged rehearsals began with manned flights on Saturn V. In other words, the test flights would follow a sequential integration pattern rather than concurrently overlapping.

Above: *On the second manned Gemini flight, on 3 June 1965, NASA astronaut Ed White conducts the first American EVA, almost three months after the Soviet Union's Alexei Leonov becomes the first man to exit a spacecraft in orbit.*

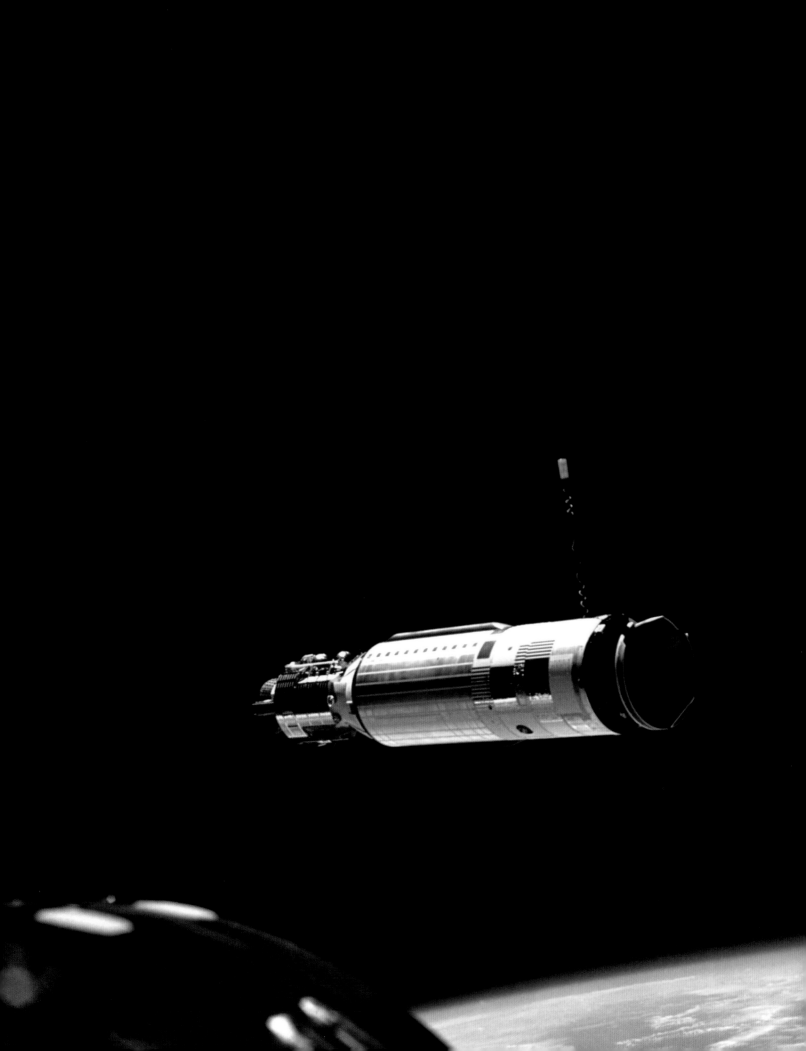

Phillips insisted on implementing his "all-up systems testing" philosophy that had worked so well with the three-stage Minuteman missile. Instead of flying several rockets to test the first stage, then several more to test the first and second stage before finally flying all three live stages, from the very first launch the Saturn V would fly with three fully fuelled and operating stages. Today, that seems quite logical; in 1963 it was radical. Then, rockets were still failing at an alarming rate, and to pay for completely assembled and equipped upper stages that were likely to be destroyed in the inevitable learning curve seemed foolish. But Mueller insisted, and only by degrees did the von Braun team, with its entrenched conservatism, acquiesce. It would turn out to be the single enabling decision that ensured the success of the programme.

Before Apollo was ready for test flights, first on Saturn IB and then with Saturn V, there were ten manned Gemini flights, following two unmanned launches in 1964 and early 1965. The first Gemini crew were launched on 23 March 1965, a three-orbit mission to demonstrate the performance of the spacecraft. This was followed by Gemini IV on 3 June, a four-day mission during which Ed White became the first American to conduct a spacewalk. Gemini V was launched on 21 August for a mission that lasted almost eight days and tested the fuel-cell concept for electrical power production. Fuel cells would power the Apollo spacecraft and all 135 Shuttle missions, a pioneering product of the Space Age.

Gemini VI, in October, was to have been the first rendezvous and docking flight, but the Atlas-Agena aiming to put the target vehicle in orbit failed and the Gemini launch was postponed. Gemini VII was next, a 14-day endurance mission launched on 4 December, during which Gemini VI-A was launched to rendezvous with Gemini VII – two vehicles controlled separately from Houston, demonstrating that one vehicle could chase after another and meet up with it in orbit.

A first docking mission was launched on 16 March 1966 but, after achieving this with a previously launched target vehicle, the Gemini VIII spacecraft suffered a technical problem and the astronauts (Armstrong and Scott, both future Apollo commanders) had to return to Earth prematurely. Next up, Gemini IX launched on 3 June 1966 to attempt a docking but, finding the protective shroud still attached, the mission ended without accomplishing that task. It also brought home the difficulties with life-support backpacks when astronaut Gene Cernan's visor fogged up and he was unable to try his hand on a jetpack to which he had attached himself.

The last three Gemini flights went ahead successfully, each a docking mission with several periods of EVA: Gemini X on 18 July, when the Agena propulsion system was used to change orbit for the first time; Gemini XI launched on 12 September, with the Agena's main engine pushing the docked vehicles to an all-time Earth-orbit altitude record of 850 miles (1,369km); and Gemini XII sent up on 11 November 1966, allowing Buzz Aldrin to demonstrate that the way to conduct successful weightless spacewalks was to have a satisfactory tether and restraint system so that the body conserves energy that is otherwise wasted on trying to maintain position.

Left: *An Agena target vehicle prior to docking by a Gemini spacecraft, demonstrating that two vehicles in space could not only find each other but dock into a rigid structure – an essential element required by the Apollo mission.*

By the end of 1966, the United States had completed 16 manned space flights in less than six years, all but two being Earth orbit missions during which NASA had leapt far ahead of the Soviets. Many problems that had beset the organization appeared to be evaporating. Technical progress had been made in demonstrating how humans could survive in space long enough to reach the Moon and return, to seek out and dock with other vehicles already in space, and in conducting spacewalks on an almost routine basis. The launch vehicles too were ready.

The Saturn IB had made its first flight on 26 February 1966, with improved and slightly more powerful H-1 engines in the first stage and the powerful J-2 in the S-IVB upper stage. A second flight on 5 July had successfully demonstrated that the design of the S-IVB was fit for restarts in space, as would be required when that stage was used on a Saturn V, and a third flight on 25 August 1966 had been the first successful test of an unmanned Apollo spacecraft.

Even as the last Gemini mission was returning to Earth on 15 November 1966, astronauts Gus Grissom, Ed White and Roger Chaffee were preparing for the first manned Earth orbit flight of the Apollo spacecraft on the fourth Saturn IB at Cape Canaveral. Elsewhere, everything was coming together for the first launch of the giant Saturn V, all three stages to be live in accordance with Phillips's all-up testing. Confidence was high and the general public sensed the pace was picking up. Humans really could reach the Moon by the end of the decade. What could possibly go wrong?

Opposite: *Astronauts Armstrong and Scott return to a Pacific Ocean splashdown from their Gemini VIII mission. This angle reveals the small amount of space in which Borman and Lovell had spent two weeks in December 1965.*

Below: *In December 1965 two Gemini spacecraft rendezvous in orbit, demonstrating an essential element of the Apollo mission plan, when the Lunar Module would leave the lunar surface and search out the Apollo mother ship.*

CHAPTER 4

THE RISE OF APOLLO

It was 6.30 p.m. on Friday evening, 27 January 1967. The lights were on around Launch Complex 34 at Cape Canaveral, where a Saturn IB rocket stood ready for a simulated test involving the first Apollo crew. They were little more than three weeks away from an Earth orbit shakedown mission to test out the new three-man spacecraft, and dress rehearsals were just one part of the busy schedule involving testing, training, "flying" the simulators and honing procedures.

Designated CSM-012, this particular vehicle was not quite the configuration that Moon-bound Apollo spacecraft would have because NASA had decided to fast-track a Block I version, carrying only the bare essentials for a simple Earth-orbit proving flight. The fully equipped Block II version carrying systems necessary for flying to the Moon and back, such as docking probes and further-developed navigation software, would come later. Moreover, this launch on a Saturn IB would be one of several then planned to prepare the way for flights on the mighty Saturn V.

With a thrust of 1.6 million lb (7,119kN), the Saturn IB was little more than one-fifth the power of the Saturn V assigned to send both the Apollo mother-ship and the Lunar Module to the Moon. But Saturn V had yet to fly unmanned and the Saturn IB would be sufficient to lift an Apollo into low Earth orbit where the spacecraft could be put through its paces. It was an essential precursor bridging the just-completed Gemini flights and the lunar missions to follow.

"WE'VE GOT A FIRE IN THE COCKPIT!"

Working towards a launch date of 21 February 1967, the Grissom crew had entered their spacecraft on top of its Saturn IB at Cape Canaveral around 1.00 p.m. on Friday, 27 January. It was to be what NASA called a plugs-out test, in which the spacecraft would run on internal power and proceed through the various phases of a countdown, stopping just before launch. But it was a "dry" test, with no propellant in either the rocket or the spacecraft. Ironically, it was intended to end with a rehearsal of an emergency escape from the spacecraft and the vicinity of the Saturn IB, practising a procedure they never wanted to carry out in reality.

After countless communications and systems problems that made it virtually impossible for the crew and the test supervisors to hear each other, Gus Grissom

Above: *NASA selected (left to right) Gus Grissom, Ed White and Roger Chaffee to fly the first manned Apollo mission. Grissom had flown the second suborbital Mercury shot in 1961 and the first Gemini mission in 1965. White had performed America's first spacewalk on the second Gemini mission in 1965. Chaffee had never flown in space before.*

murmured into his helmet microphone in frustration: "How are we gonna get to the Moon if we can't talk between three buildings…?" Ed White growled his concurrence, doubting that anybody could hear him anyway! Less than three minutes later an electrical short resulted in a fire starting on the lower side of the left couch where Grissom was lying in his position as spacecraft commander; to his right was Ed White and then Roger Chaffee.

Because the capsule was pressured above atmospheric pressure to prevent any nitrogen leaking in from outside, the pure oxygen accelerated the propagation of the fire, raising the pressure still further. In less than 30 seconds the crew were asphyxiated by the toxic smoke filling the cabin, cardiac failure following. Seconds later the pressure inside became so great that it split the base of the capsule, smoke pouring out on to the enclosed work platform at the top of the rocket, an action which smothered the fire.

Above: *The interior of the Apollo Command Module after the bodies of Grissom, White and Chaffee had been removed following the catastrophic fire on 27 January 1967.*

Left: *The blackened exterior of the spacecraft is evidence of the cloud of smoke and carbon monoxide that had escaped from the Command Module when it split at the base as the internal pressure increased to 29lb/sq in (200kPa). The lattice structure is the tower for the Launch Escape System, carried by all the spacecraft to lift the crew free if anything went wrong after launch and before achieving orbit.*

In the investigation that followed, NASA never conclusively identified the cause of the fire, many believing from detailed forensic examination of the spacecraft that it began in some electrical component of the environmental control system. Others disagreed and pointed a finger at the communication line to Grissom's suit, known as the "cobra cable" because of its shape. All communication required a crew member to switch on his or her voice line, but Grissom's had remained open all the way through the test until it suddenly switched back to switch-mode seconds before the first call of "Fire!"

Above: *Grim faces at the witness table before a Senate committee on the Apollo 1 accident (left to right): Dr Robert C. Seamans, NASA Deputy Administrator; James E. Webb, NASA Administrator; Dr George E. Mueller, Associate Administrator for Manned Space; and Maj. Gen. Samuel C. Phillips, Apollo Program Director.*

PHOENIX RISING

Shock ran throughout NASA and spilled out across the nation. And as if to hammer home the inherent danger of space flight, the Soviet cosmonaut Vladimir Komarov lost his life in the first Soyuz spacecraft when it crashed to Earth on 24 April 1967. The grief was now shared among ideological protagonists who had sought to play out their struggle for the admiration of mankind in ever-more-dramatic space spectaculars.

After an exhaustive inquiry with evidence from scientists, engineers and those who had meticulously taken the Apollo spacecraft apart, piece by piece, in parallel with disassembly of another Block I Command Module for comparison, it was decided only to fly the definitive Block II on future missions. Block I had too many inconsistencies and as an intermediate test vehicle it was littered with pieces of equipment which, once wired in and later removed when it was decided they were not needed, left cables still in the wiring looms, coming from nowhere and going nowhere.

Poor quality control had been a factor in the Apollo disaster and an exhaustive and widespread programme of recertification of materials and removal of flammable sources dramatically transformed the safety of the spacecraft. In test mock-ups, fires were deliberately started to test their ability to self-extinguish and a special fire-suppression system was built in to Block II spacecraft. Wiring was potted so that any shorts or sparks would be contained within the protective sheathing. None of the 21 miles (33.7km) of wiring in the Command Module alone would ever again pose a fire threat to the crew. Even the flight plans were made of fireproof paper!

There was significant progress with preparing the Saturn V for its inaugural flight, an event that took place when the biggest rocket built to this day sent thunder across Cape Canaveral on 9 November 1967, blasting Launch Complex 39A with a thrust of 7.5 million lb (33,360kN). At the CBS broadcasting booth, anchorman Walter Cronkite had to hold the plasterboard ceiling up with his hand as the shock waves from 3 miles (5km) away threatened to tear down the building from which he was broadcasting. Nothing like Saturn V had ever been experienced before, but the three stages performed flawlessly, sending the unmanned Block I Apollo spacecraft on a looping trajectory 11,242 miles (18,092km) out before the Command Module came slicing back through the atmosphere to demonstrate the integrity of the heat shield.

In commemoration of the tragic loss of Grissom, White and Chaffee, NASA retained the designation of Apollo 1 for that first intended manned flight. The two unmanned Block I Apollo spacecraft previously launched by Saturn IB rockets (see Chapter 3) were retrospectively designated Apollo 2 and 3, and the first Saturn V flight became Apollo 4. With delays caused by the Apollo 1 investigation and the modifications and recertification of the Bock II configuration, future mission planning underwent a complete revision.

Apollo 5 was launched on 22 January 1968, a Saturn IB carrying the first Lunar Module on an unmanned Earth-orbit shakedown flight, followed by the second unmanned Saturn V flight on 4 April. Designated Apollo 6, the mission was a success, but some technical problems nearly destroyed the rocket. Resonant acoustic frequencies caused a "pogo" effect, with the launcher pulsating up and down as it ascended, shaking loose some pipes which shut down two of the five second-stage engines. But the primary objectives were accomplished and engineers saw no reason not to send astronauts on the very next Saturn V flight.

THE RISE OF APOLLO **63**

MISSION SHUFFLES

By mid-1967 the backup crew to the Grissom mission knew they would be the first astronauts to ride the Apollo spacecraft into orbit on a Saturn IB – essentially flying the mission planned for Apollo 1. It would fall to Schirra, Eisele and Cunningham to shake down the Block II spacecraft and prepare the way to the Moon. The mission would be known as Apollo 7 and it would turn out to be quite contentious.

During the first half of 1968, after the first LM had been test-flown unmanned in the Earth's orbit and judged satisfactory for the next phase of flight evaluation, Grumman began to proclaim difficulties with preparing the first manned LM for delivery. Delays set in and it began to look as though the entire programme was in danger of missing the deadline for reaching the surface. With only 18 months to go, Grumman could not guarantee that Apollo 8 would have a Lunar Module to test. This was when a radical idea emerged, one so secret that only a few top NASA officials were in on it.

Below: *Astronauts (left to right) Don F. Eisele, Walter M. Schirra and Walter Cunningham moved from the backup slot for Apollo 1 to the prime crew for Apollo 7, conducting a 10-day shakedown flight to demonstrate the ability for the spacecraft to support a three-man crew for the duration of a Moon mission.*

A HOME FOR THREE

The Apollo spacecraft consisted of two parts – the Command Module (CM) and the Service Module (SM) – which would remain attached together for the entire duration of the flight until just before re-entry into Earth's atmosphere. Only the CM was habitable, but all the life-support, electrical power, communications equipment and propulsion for the entire mission was contained in the SM, which served as the engine room of the Apollo spacecraft, a self-contained space vehicle capable of docking with the Lunar Module.

The conical-shape Command Module had a pressurized interior, which could support three crew members for up to 14 days. It was 11.42ft (3.48m) in height and 12.83ft (3.91m) in diameter. To save weight and simplify the systems, the spacecraft was pressurized with pure oxygen at slightly more than one-third atmospheric pressure measured at the Earth's surface, 14.7lb/sq in (101.35kPa) of which 3lb/sq in (20.68kPa) is oxygen. To provide sufficient oxygen for the human body, the interior of the spacecraft was pressurized at 5lb/sq in (34.47kPa). For spacewalking, the suits would be pressurized to 3.5lb/sq in (24.13kPa), as low as possible to retain maximum flexibility and just above the critical threshold for crew health and safety.

The Command Module weighed around 12,500lb (5,670kg) and a lot of that weight went into the heat shield that would protect it during re-entry, against heat produced by kinetic energy as the module sliced into the atmosphere at 25,000mph (40,225km/h). The flat underbody of the cone-shaped module kept the shock wave created by re-entry clear of the surface of the spacecraft, thus exposing the shield to much less heat than registered in the shock wave itself. The heat shield consisted of a stainless-steel honeycomb matrix with each

Opposite: The Apollo heat shield contained 370,000 honeycomb cells, into each of which was injected a phenolic epoxy resin to provide an ablative layer that would gradually char away as it heated on re-entry. Its thickness was sufficient not to completely burn through from friction with the atmosphere.

Below: This cross-section shows how the various layers of the Apollo Command Module heat shield protected the pressurized interior where the crew resided.

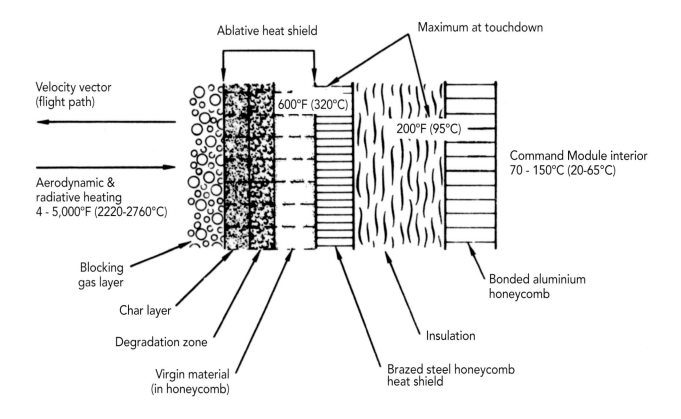

Ablative heat shield

Maximum at touchdown

Velocity vector
(flight path)

600°F (320°C)

200°F (95°C)

Command Module interior
70 - 150°C (20-65°C)

Aerodynamic &
radiative heating
4 - 5,000°F (2220-2760°C)

Blocking
gas layer

Char layer

Degradation zone

Virgin material
(in honeycomb)

Brazed steel honeycomb
heat shield

Insulation

Bonded aluminium
honeycomb

cell filled with a phenolic epoxy resin. Thickness varied proportional to the expected temperature across different parts of the exterior surface with the maximum depth about 2.5in (6.35cm).

The Service Module was a cylindrical drum-shaped structure 12.92ft (3.94m) in length and 12.83ft (3.91m) in diameter with a central tunnel 44in (1.12m) in diameter. Located in the lower section of the tunnel was the Service Propulsion System (SPS), a liquid propellant rocket motor with a thrust of 20,700lb (92.1kN) which was used for all major orbital and translunar manoeuvres and which would be employed to brake the docked CM/LM vehicles into lunar orbit and return the CSM back on course for Earth. Propellant for the SPS engine was contained in two fuel and two oxidizer tanks occupying four of six pie-segments in the Service Module. The total length of the SM with rocket engine and nozzle attached was 24.16ft (7.34m).

When fully fuelled with approximately 40,700lb (18.460kg) of propellant for the SPS engine and 850lb (385kg) of propellant for the 16 attitude-control and manoeuvring thrusters, located in four quads at 90° intervals on the exterior, the Service Module had a launch weight of about 51,200lb (23,224kg). Together with the Command Module, this gave the Apollo spacecraft a total weight of about 63,700lb (28,894kg).

What if, instead of flying their highly elliptical orbit much like the unmanned Apollo 4 flight, the Borman, Lovell and Anders crew, planning to carry out their mission as Apollo 9, jumped ahead of the planned McDivitt crew, intensely rehearsing their Lunar Module Earth-orbit mission? What if, on a mission redesignated Apollo 8, they flew all the way to the Moon and either went right around it and came straight back or, even more audaciously, went into orbit for a day before returning home? That would keep up momentum, test out the Apollo spacecraft on its own in the domain for which it was designed, and allow time for Grumman to ready the LM for what was now going to be Apollo 9.

Left: *The Apollo spacecraft consisted of a pressurized Command Module, here wrapped in blue tape to protect the heat shield, and the Service Module containing all the life-support, communications and propulsion equipment.*

Below: *The launch of Apollo 7 on 11 October 1968. Responding to concerns about pure oxygen at atmospheric pressure, the spacecraft was pressurized at 60 per cent oxygen and 40 per cent nitrogen for launch, bled out during ascent and replaced with pure oxygen at the much safer one-third atmospheric pressure by the time it achieved orbit.*

Above: *The crew of Apollo 7 look down on the S-IVB second stage of the Saturn IB that placed them in orbit as they pass across Cape Canaveral almost 186 miles (300km) below.*

It all depended on how well the Apollo 7 flight went. Leaving the launch pad on 11 October 1968, this was technically near perfect, managed by a crew who performed everything expected; however, they were plagued by some disorientation as they floated around their more spacious spacecraft and had difficulties with the "waste management system", which had all the attractiveness of an open sewer! On what was intended to be a shakedown flight, the crew grew testy with pesky annoyances that built up, an attitude made worse when Schirra went down with a severe head cold. In what was the first but certainly not the last time a crew challenged Mission Control in a manner bordering on mutiny, the media demand for live TV shows – the first from a US spacecraft – sent Schirra into open rebellion, dictating to ground controllers exactly when he would and would not transmit tours of the spacecraft interior. Punctuated with a degree of humour but with a pithy disregard for being told what to do, the crew came home after just over 10 days, 20 hours in space. None of them would fly again.

Above: *Having proved that the Apollo Block II spacecraft was capable of supporting manned missions and that its systems operated effectively, the crew splashed down on Earth on 22 October, clearing the way for a manned flight around the Moon.*

Right: *The pressurized Command Module contained three collapsible couches. When folded away, they provided room for moving around and for accessing the navigation station on the opposite wall to the entry hatch. For Block II this was a unified quick-release design for rapid escape in emergency on the ground. The old Block I hatch was in three sections and took 90 seconds to open, one reason why the crew of Apollo 1 could not escape in time.*

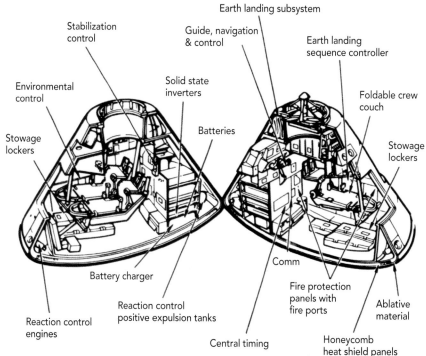

Stabilization control

Environmental control

Stowage lockers

Solid state inverters

Batteries

Guide, navigation & control

Earth landing subsystem

Earth landing sequence controller

Foldable crew couch

Stowage lockers

Battery charger

Reaction control engines

Reaction control positive expulsion tanks

Central timing

Comm

Fire protection panels with fire ports

Honeycomb heat shield panels

Ablative material

POWER TO THE PEOPLE

Oxygen to breathe, electrical power to run the spacecraft, and water both for cooling the temperature of equipment and purified for drinking and reconstituting dehydrated food all came from a single integrated system involving two tanks of liquid hydrogen and two of liquid oxygen. It was unique in all of spacecraft design.

The Service Module carried these four tanks in pairs on separate shelves in one of the pie-shaped segments. Brought together over a nitrogen catalyst, the hydrogen and oxygen produced electrical power and water as a by-product. This operates on the principle of reverse-electrolysis: instead of using an electrical charge to split water into its molecular components of hydrogen and oxygen, those constituents are brought together over a catalyst to produce power in fuel cells, three of which were mounted on a separate shelf. Nowadays, the fuel cell is one alternative to hydrocarbon fuels, providing "green" energy to drive vehicles, but fuel cells have powered NASA manned spacecraft since Gemini V in August 1966.

Water produced in this process was used for cooling electrical and electronic equipment and for dispensing through a spigot to rehydrate packaged food. In purified form, it was used for drinking too. The oxygen to breathe also came from one of the two tanks, the liquid turning to gas in the warmth of the equipment installed to deliver it to the pressurized crew compartment of the Command Module. Apollo pioneered great strides in spacecraft technology and this principle carried forward to the Shuttle, except in that vehicle the crew breathed a mixture of oxygen and nitrogen as humans do on Earth.

Below: *The general proportions of the Apollo Service Module with its six pie-shaped segments. Four contained propellant tanks for the main SPS engine, while a fifth supported the three fuel cells and the two oxygen and two hydrogen reactant tanks for producing electrical energy and water as a by-product.*

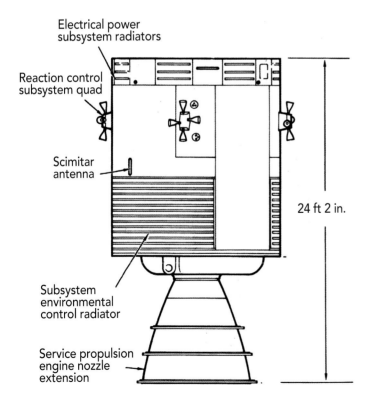

Electrical power subsystem radiators

Reaction control subsystem quad

Scimitar antenna

Subsystem environmental control radiator

Service propulsion engine nozzle extension

24 ft 2 in.

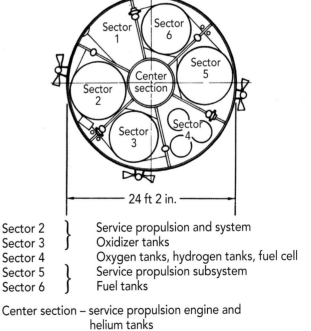

24 ft 2 in.

Sector 1   Sector 6   Sector 5   Center section   Sector 2   Sector 3   Sector 4

Sector 2 }	Service propulsion and system
Sector 3 }	Oxidizer tanks
Sector 4	Oxygen tanks, hydrogen tanks, fuel cell
Sector 5 }	Service propulsion subsystem
Sector 6 }	Fuel tanks

Center section – service propulsion engine and helium tanks

CHAPTER 5

GETTING READY

Not everybody working to reach the Moon was American – either by birth or by citizenship. In the late 1950s a group of Canadians headed south when the call went out from NASA for qualified aircraft engineers to help build the mission control and communications networks for the one-man Mercury programme. Having lost their jobs when the Canadian government cancelled a supersonic interceptor known as the Avro Canada CF-105, they were grateful for this new and exciting opportunity. Among them was John Hodge, who would work with Christopher Kraft and Eugene "Gene" Kranz to build NASA's human space flight programme. Another was James Chamberlin, an early convert to Lunar Orbit Rendezvous who became Gemini Program Manager, while CF-105 refugee Owen Maynard made his own special mark on the programme.

Below: *The Mission Operations Control Room where flights were directed and managed. Here, William Schneider, Chris Kraft and John Hodge (standing, left to right) are talking to Gene Kranz (seated) during one of the Gemini missions.*

Above: *John Hodge migrated to the United States after a Canadian fighter-aircraft project he was working on was cancelled. He participated as a Flight Director on several Gemini missions and played a major role in the development of flight operations in NASA's Houston facility.*

Above: *With its sights set on the Moon, NASA prepared major new facilities for launching Saturn V rockets. The Vehicle Assembly Building, the largest on Earth at the time it was constructed in the mid-1960s, dominates the foreground. Here, the Saturn V/Apollo was assembled and rolled out to one of the launch pads (top) along the Crawlerway.*

Maynard was recruited by Robert Piland to head up a small group working on post-Mercury spacecraft configurations and was one of the creative originators of the Apollo spacecraft design in 1960 – more than a year before Kennedy propelled it to a lofty goal! Three years later he headed up the Lunar Module engineering office in Houston. But Maynard is perhaps remembered most for his roadmap to achieving a Moon landing, set down in September 1967 and defined by a series of steps, each denoted by a letter of the alphabet.

Unmanned Command/Service Module qualification flights would be mission A, accomplished by the Apollo 4 and Apollo 6 Saturn V missions. The initial unmanned demonstration of the Lunar Module was mission type B, flown as Apollo 5. This would be followed by the first manned demonstration

Above: *The 36-storey Saturn V was assembled in a stack on the Mobile Launch Platform, under which moved the Crawler Transporter to carry it to Launch Complex 39, where it was launched. Up to four rockets could be stacked in the VAB simultaneously.*

Left: *The Mobile Launch Platforms contained separate rooms inside for connecting fuel, hydraulic, pneumatic and electrical utilities at the pad with the rocket when it arrived and plugged in. Three MLPs were built, each with a Launch Umbilical Tower at one end, which carried servicing conduits to various stages of the rocket and spacecraft.*

flight of a CSM, mission C, achieved by Apollo 7. The next step would be a manned Saturn V flight of the CSM and LM together in low Earth orbit, mission D, followed by a repeat flight but to a highly elliptical orbit with a maximum altitude of 4,039 miles (6,500km), known as mission E. A full dress rehearsal in Moon orbit would be mission F, followed by the initial landing as mission G. Later, more advanced Apollo missions would build on that alphabet.

It all worked out just as Maynard had predicted, except for one change when mission E jumped ahead of mission D and went all the way to the Moon and back in one of the boldest and most risky flights ever mounted by NASA. But that was not a simple decision to make. The second flight of an unmanned Saturn V, Apollo 6 (see previous chapter), came perilously close to failure, and so the manager of the Apollo spacecraft programme office, George M. Low, made a bold recommendation indeed when he suggested launching astronauts to the Moon on the very next Saturn V flight. They soon came round to his thinking. But it still required the approval of NASA boss, Jim Webb.

If implemented, it would require the next Apollo crew to fly the first manned Saturn V trusting that modifications implemented to prevent a repeat of Apollo 6 had been successful – there would be no test flight for those improvements. But the change was dictated when the Lunar Module for what was then Apollo 8 (Mission D) arrived at the Cape in June and technicians noted a range of problems that threatened to push its flight beyond the end of the year.

Above: *The Crawler Transporter had a total length of 131.25ft (40m) and a width of 114ft (34.7m) with eight crawler tracks, each shoe of which weighed 1 tonne.*

Opposite: *At the launch pad, the sheer scale of the MLP/ULT is seen here, towering almost 500ft (152m) above the ground. To the right is the equally massive Mobile Service Structure, moved up to the rocket for technicians to gain access to the Saturn V, and withdrawn before launch.*

THE HEAVY LIFTER

The race to the Moon forced into play technologies not yet invented when President Kennedy directed NASA to put astronauts on the lunar surface. Several of these essential engineering inventions were developed for the Saturn V – still today the biggest and most powerful launch vehicle ever used operationally. One such technology, enabling a single rocket to send astronauts to the Moon, was the evolution of the highly efficient cryogenic liquid oxygen/liquid hydrogen rocket motor. Through the use of cryogenic propellants in the second and third stages, the lifting potential of this rocket was equal to a very much bigger launchers using more conventional but less efficient propellants.

NASA was a world leader in the use of cryogenic propellants, developing the Centaur stage for a variety of launch vehicles – and that stage is still flying today. After the first cryogenic stage ever sent into space was carried on the fifth Saturn I flight on 29 January 1964, the door was open on further development of the more powerful S-IVB stage, which was also used as the third stage of the Saturn V. It was this stage, and the J-2 rocket motor, that made such a big difference to the payload lifting capability of the Saturn V.

While five F-1 engines delivering a total thrust of 7.5 million lb (33,360kN) and burning kerosene and liquid oxygen were used in the S-IC first stage, the S-II second stage carried five J-2 engines, delivering a total thrust of 1 million lb (4,448kN), with the S-IVB third stage powered

Above: *The Douglas S-IVB third stage carried a single J-2 cryogenic motor. Note that the tanks containing the fuel and the oxidizer are separated by a common bulkhead to better insulate the super-cold liquids.*

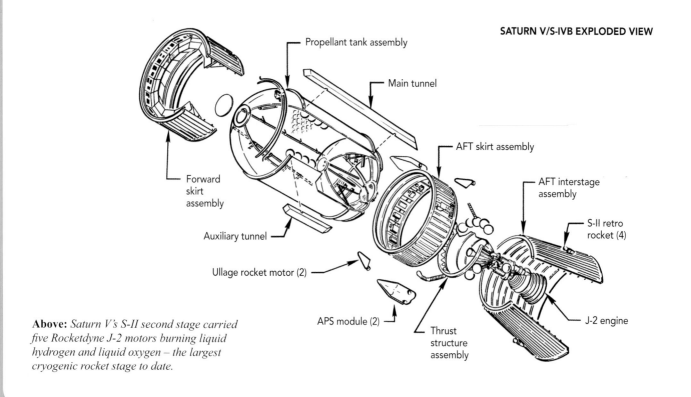

SATURN V/S-IVB EXPLODED VIEW

- Propellant tank assembly
- Main tunnel
- AFT skirt assembly
- AFT interstage assembly
- S-II retro rocket (4)
- Forward skirt assembly
- Auxiliary tunnel
- Ullage rocket motor (2)
- APS module (2)
- Thrust structure assembly
- J-2 engine

Above: *Saturn V's S-II second stage carried five Rocketdyne J-2 motors burning liquid hydrogen and liquid oxygen – the largest cryogenic rocket stage to date.*

by one J-2 delivering a thrust of 200,000lb (889.6kN). The Saturn V was so powerful that it was capable of lifting into orbit a weight equivalent to all 16 previously launched US manned spacecraft on a single flight. As Saturn V flights progressed and weight-saving measures were introduced, improvements to the performance of the rocket motors increased the stage thrust levels, allowing slightly heavier spacecraft to be carried.

The colossal size of the 36-storey rocket is best appreciated by the amount of propellant it carried, around 2,540 tonnes, or 960,000gal (3.63 million litres). Put another way, a small and efficient petrol car today could drive to the Moon and back 90 times on that amount! But elimination of unnecessary wiring was a prime concern. If each wire soldered to a joint was $\frac{1}{32}$ inch too long, the excess weight on all 2.5 million connections would equal the entire payload of the rocket!

But Saturn V required special facilities and, unlike previous launch vehicles, its size and complexity meant it needed to be assembled first into a vertical "stack" involving all the separate stages and spacecraft before roll-out to the launch pad. That required construction of the Vehicle Assembly Building (VAB), a vast enclosure of 129.428 million cu ft (3.665 million cu m). At the time it was built, this was the largest ever man-made enclosure, big enough to contain all the pyramids of Egypt's Giza plateau.

The launch pad was located more than 3 miles (4.8km) from the VAB so that an explosion there would not bring it down. A special Crawler Transporter, the largest land-moving vehicle at the time with a weight of 2,700 tonnes, supported a Mobile Launch Platform, which itself weighed 4,760 tonnes, together with an unrefuelled Saturn V weighing about 59 tonnes. The combined moving mass of approximately 7,519 tonnes would move to the launch pad at a maximum speed of 2mph (3.2km/h), taking a full day to make the journey.

Once there, the Crawler Transporter would place the Mobile Launch Platform on pedestals and withdraw to collect the Mobile Service Structure (MSS). With a weight of 5,443 tonnes, it was brought up to the Mobile Launch Platform and placed alongside the Saturn V so that technicians could use it to service the rocket. The combined weight of all this hardware placed nearly 13,000 tonnes on the pad. The MSS would be removed prior to flight, after which the Saturn V would be fuelled with propellant, increasing its weight to almost 3,000 tonnes.

Below: *Saturn V S-IC first stages are assembled in NASA's Michoud Assembly Facility by Boeing workers under contract to the space agency. Using kerosene and liquid oxygen propellants, the S-IC was the world's largest and most powerful rocket.*

If NASA waited to launch Apollo 8 as a proving flight for the Lunar Module, Borman's Apollo 9 flight (Mission E) would have to wait until the second quarter of 1969 – leaving less time for problems prior to the landing attempt.

Within three days, approval had been given, and preparations accelerated in great secrecy as Webb forbade any reference to the plan prior to the flight of Apollo 7. But the spacecraft would have to be switched around because the Apollo 8 spacecraft had the docking probe and software for that mission, so the original D mission designated Apollo 8 became Apollo 9, pre-empted by Borman's crew flying to the Moon as a modified E mission. There was one further proviso insisted upon by Webb: when made public, the mission would not be referred to as an E mission, out of sequence, but as a C (C-prime) mission instead.

Below: *Inside one of the four Firing Rooms, where approximately 450 people controlled the launch of a Saturn V/Apollo stack. It was from here that flights were managed until after lift-off was completed.*

AUDACITY AND RESOLUTION

Much has been made of the influence of intelligence information concerning Soviet space plans, but only officials at the very highest levels in NASA were concerned about that. Test flights with the circumlunar Zond ship had begun in March 1967 and the first attempted lunar fly-by with an unmanned test vehicle came on 28 September 1967. It failed, as did more attempts until a biological payload including two tortoises, launched on 14 September 1968, circumnavigated the Moon.

Nevertheless, with Apollo 7 out of the way and the spacecraft itself cleared for more ambitious objectives, only an intensive analysis of flight data from this first manned mission stood in the way of a circumlunar flight. Three weeks after the Apollo 7 crew returned, NASA formally announced on 12 November 1968 that the next Apollo flight would not only be the first manned Saturn V launch but would also be the first human flight into deep space.

Contrary to expectations among the outer circle privy to something spectacular being planned, however, Apollo 8 would not fly around the Moon – it would go into lunar orbit and spend around 20 hours photographing the surface and evaluating the performance of the spacecraft. That was a new level of risk and audacity. By going into orbit around the Moon, the big SPS engine in the back of the Apollo Service Module would have to fire to decelerate the spacecraft instead of allowing it to whip around the Moon and come straight back to Earth as Zond had done. That in itself brought a potential hazard. If the engine burned too long it would decelerate the spacecraft too much, sending it crashing to the lunar surface. And if it failed to fire again to accelerate Apollo out of lunar orbit and back to Earth, that would be fatal. The small manoeuvring thrusters sufficiently powerful to make orbital corrections on a simple fly-by would be incapable of propelling Apollo out of lunar orbit. Without the SPS engine they would be stuck – and there would be nothing that could be done about it.

Above: *Preparation for launch and lift-off was controlled from one of four Firing Rooms in the Launch Control Center, located alongside the Vehicle Assembly Building. Only when the Saturn V cleared the Launch Umbilical Tower did flight control pass to the Manned Spacecraft Center (now the Johnson Space Center) in Houston.*

CHAPTER 6

LEAVING EARTH

The countdown for Apollo 8 began after dusk on Sunday, 15 December and already the first visitors had arrived, setting up camp on the beaches along Merritt Island and within view of Pad 39 at the Kennedy Space Center, the northern zone of Cape Canaveral. By launch day they would be joined by a multitude numbering hundreds of thousands.

On 21 December the crew of Borman, Lovell and Anders had been awake since 2.36 a.m. and, after a brief medical check, had breakfast before moving to the suit-up room where, 45 minutes later, they were completely attired in their space suits. Then it was out to the transfer van and a drive to the pad, arriving just after 5.00 a.m. Ten minutes later they were at the top of the Saturn

Above: *Simplicity itself, the Apollo 8 badge represented the circumlunar path of Apollo 8 within the conical shape of the Command Module, a design sketched out by Jim Lovell while flying in the back seat in a NASA T-38 trainer, later formalized by artist William Bradley of Houston, Texas.*

Opposite: *The first flight to orbit the Moon with astronauts included (left to right) Command Module Pilot Jim Lovell, Lunar Module Pilot William "Bill" Anders and Mission Commander Frank Borman. The crew of Apollo 8 were originally to have flown Apollo 9, testing the Lunar Module and Apollo spacecraft in a high, elliptical orbit. The LM was not ready, but the crew designation remained when the astronauts flew ahead of the first manned LM flight.*

Left: *Suiting up for Apollo 8, Frank Borman had his initial expedition in command of Gemini 7 in December 1965, the first flight to spend two weeks in space. The Moon left Borman cold, with no desire to land on its surface. This would be his last mission.*

V in the White Room, a box-like enclosure fitting tightly to the exterior of the Apollo Command Module. From there they began to enter the spacecraft, strap in and hook up all the leads and connectors for oxygen, communications, biomedical data flow and electrical power.

Lift-off came at precisely 7.51 a.m. after a lengthy automated countdown and only seconds after all the tracking stations and emergency pickup forces around the world had given their "go" for launch. Ignition came at T-8.9 seconds in the count: the five F-1 engines fired, and computers checked out several thousand data readings to clear the vehicle for release and lift-off at zero on the clock. The vibration of ignition and the first few seconds off the pad shattered almost one tonne of frozen condensation which had frosted on the outside of the rocket's cryogenic tanks, sending it cascading to the ground in flakes and chunks of ice.

To dowse the fire and the heat from launch, 29 nozzles sprayed 830gal (1,250 litres) of water each second on to the hot steel of the pad, with the retracted swing-arms on the Launch Umbilical Tower steaming as other jets sprayed more water on these lattice conduits. To those watching from afar, the few seconds of flight brought concern as the vehicle appeared to be leaning over, away from the tower – which was what it designed to do, the guidance system momentarily steering it away from any potential collision with the umbilical structure alongside.

Above: *The Apollo 8 flight crew depart the Manned Spacecraft Operations Building at the Kennedy Space Center to board the transfer van for the drive to Launch Complex 39A.*

Opposite: *Lift-off, into a clear sky on the morning of 21 December 1968 on the first human space flight beyond the Earth's radiation belts and into deep space. Never before had humans been in lunar orbit.*

For the crew, in their position more than 20 storeys high up the stack, the sheer violence and vibration was very much an experience to ride out in the 2min 53sec it took to consume the 2,000 tonnes of kerosene and liquid oxygen carried by the first stage tanks at ignition. Burning 13 tonnes of propellant each second, the weight of the giant Saturn V had been reduced in that period by almost one-third. To those on the ground,` it was as unique an experience as it was for the crew, thunderclaps of sound reverberating off the concrete pad and sending shock waves across the flat wetlands of Cape Canaveral to pound on the VIPs watching a mere 5 miles (8km) away.

When the S-IC shut down, it separated from the rest of the stack, and powerful retrorockets down at the base of the first stage fired briefly to decelerate the now inert hulk, which, even empty, weighed 173 tonnes and could do catastrophic damage if it were to shunt into the base of the second stage. That flash of retrofire forced a gasp of fear that the rocket had blown up. Even at a range of 56 miles (90km), the bright glow was visible. But the two remaining stages and the Apollo spacecraft were still travelling at only one-third the speed required to reach orbit and stay there without falling back to Earth.

Less than one second after the S-IC first stage fell away, the five cryogenic J-2 engines on the S-II second stage ignited, giving the crew a much smoother ride. Shortly after ignition the Launch Escape System (LES) separated from the nose of the spacecraft and fired itself away from the accelerating stages. The LES consisted of a solid-propellant rocket motor which, in the event that something went wrong on the way up, would lift the Command Module free and propel the crew to safety. From this point on, above the atmosphere, emergency escape would mean firing the big Service Propulsion System at the base of the Service Module to free the spacecraft and position it for normal recovery of the Command Module by parachute.

The second stage continued to burn for a total of 6min 8sec, pushing the remainder of the stack on to almost 90 per cent of orbital velocity, and then it separated, its own retrorockets preventing it bumping into the third stage as that fired to push the remainder of the stack into orbit 2min 36sec later, some 11min 25sec after lift-off. The S-IVB stage and Apollo

spacecraft were now in what flight controllers call a "parking orbit", a slightly elliptical path circling the Earth at 17,428mph (28,042km/h) and an average altitude of 115.6 miles (186km). For almost two orbits of the planet, crew and ground controllers checked spacecraft systems, including those of the S-IVB third stage, still attached for its final task of pushing Apollo 8 to the Moon, and refined the precise firing time to escape Earth's gravity.

Crossing the Pacific Ocean for the second time, midway between Australia and California, the S-IVB stage reignited at an elapsed time of 2hr 50min 37sec and began to push the remaining stack ever faster. From Mission Control, the command of the century had been given minutes before: "Go for TLI" – Trans-Lunar Injection, the authorization to send humans into the gravitational grasp of another world in space, a seminal moment in reaching the Moon. Dashing out into the predawn morning, radio and TV audiences on the island of Hawaii watched the bright star trail a point of light towards the horizon before bursting into sunlight.

The S-IVB burned its cryogenic propellants for 5min 19sec, pushing Apollo 8 to a speed of 24,237mph (38,998km/h) and on its way to an encounter with the Moon almost three days later. The precision with which these manoeuvres took place was extraordinary. The velocity at S-IVB

Above: *An artist visualizes the separation of the Apollo spacecraft from the S-IVB, the third stage of Saturn V. The petal-like panels supported the spacecraft on top of the Saturn V from the launch pad until separation after Trans-Lunar Injection.*

Below: *The S-IVB stage, now inert, as viewed from the Command Module. Destined to pass the Moon 784 miles (1,262km) from the surface at a mission time of almost 70 hours, it remained in an orbit of the Sun at the approximate distance of the Earth-Moon system.*

cut-off was a mere 10mph (16km/h) slower than planned, a difference that would be corrected during "mid-course manoeuvres" (MCMs). But being even that close was remarkable, for there were "residuals" from latent propellants venting down as the rocket motor shut down, a process known as "tail-off", which itself was a propulsive event that added to the overall velocity.

When the Apollo spacecraft separated from the S-IVB stage, exactly 30 minutes after S-IVB shutdown, a blip from the thrusters moved it away so that the two would not collide. Initial tracking immediately after TLI indicated that the spacecraft was on a collision course with the Moon but, after a second separation manoeuvre using the small thrusters on the Service Module, this became a miss by 527 miles (848km). That was too great for the required orbit when the spacecraft arrived, so a mid-course correction burn 11 hours into the mission, firing the powerful SPS engine for 2.4 seconds, moved the closest approach distance to 76.3 miles (122.8km).

THIS TINY OBJECT...

Passing quickly through the upper levels of the Van Allen radiation belts that surround the Earth like a doughnut, Borman, Lovell and Anders were now in the direct presence of the solar wind – that flow of energetic particles shaped around Earth by its magnetosphere, a protective shield that protects all life on Earth from the most extreme radiation. Paradoxically, the Moon missions would fly at solar maximum – that point in an 11-year cycle when solar flares are at their most intense. To deal with this, satellites had been placed in solar orbit, just inside and outside the radius of the Earth's path, to act as early-warning sensors serving notice of an impending harmful burst. Had that been received, the crew would have scurried home.

One primary task for the outbound journey was to carry out manual navigation sightings in deep space and test the theoretical simulations that had previously been conducted only in simulators or in Earth orbit. This had never been done before at such a great distance from Earth and Apollo 8 usefully pioneered it before the upcoming landings on later missions. Alignments on star sightings were obtained from the sextant and telescope installed in the wall of the Command Module opposite the hatch. The numbers were inserted on the computer keyboard situated alongside for appropriate calculations.

In the long coast to the Moon, the Apollo spacecraft would slowly rotate to ensure an even exposure to the effects of sunlight on the skin temperature of the exterior through cold-plates and cold-rails, removing heat and passing it through radiators to the outside of the Service Module. Double-skinned cold-plates and hollow cold-rails were surfaces on to which heat-producing equipment was mounted. A water-glycol coolant flowing through these surfaces would remove the excess heat and radiate it to space.

Maintaining a slow rotation around the long axis of the spacecraft, called Passive Thermal Control (PTC), evened out the temperature extremes and eased the burden on the coolant system. But there were many ways in which the balance of the spacecraft could be upset, and measuring the precise levels of those disturbances was another job for this unique mission.

During the trip out, the crew conducted two TV sessions, proving more willing and amenable to timing their transmissions to peak viewing periods in the United States than had the crew of Apollo 7. With its unique and dramatic mission, Apollo 8 drew enormous public interest and the media were infatuated with shots of the Earth growing smaller with each transmission. Displaying

personalities in tune with their role as tour guides and entertainers, all three crew members rose to the occasion, posing questions many viewers would have asked.

For example, Jim Lovell posited the query to Frank Borman: "Frank, what I keep imagining is if I am some lonely traveller from another planet, what would I think about Earth at this altitude, whether I think it would be inhabited or not? I was just curious if we would land on the blue or the brown part of the Earth."

Bill Anders replied to both: "You better hope that we land on the blue part!"

Above: *The first picture of the whole Earth taken by a handheld camera, with the spacecraft 16,640 miles (30,000km) out on its journey to the Moon.*

FINDING THE PATH

Containing more than 40,000 parts, the Guidance & Navigation (G&N) system had at its heart an inertial guidance platform from which the on-board computer would obtain information to calculate the position of the spacecraft and compute necessary course corrections. The Inertial Measurement Unit (IMU) provided a stable reference against which all motion of the spacecraft could be measured. It consisted of a platform mounted within three gimbals, or pivots, set at right angles to each other and stabilized by three gyroscopes.

Each rotation or movement of the spacecraft around the stable platform would be monitored by instruments within the IMU, determining the pitch, roll and yaw. Accelerations would be measured by three "pulsed integrating pendulous accelerometers", or PIPAs, mounted rigidly to the stable platform. A pulse train signal delivered to the computer continually updated information held on the velocity of the spacecraft. The

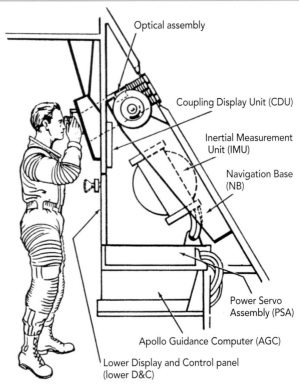

Optical assembly

Coupling Display Unit (CDU)

Inertial Measurement Unit (IMU)

Navigation Base (NB)

Power Servo Assembly (PSA)

Apollo Guidance Computer (AGC)

Lower Display and Control panel (lower D&C)

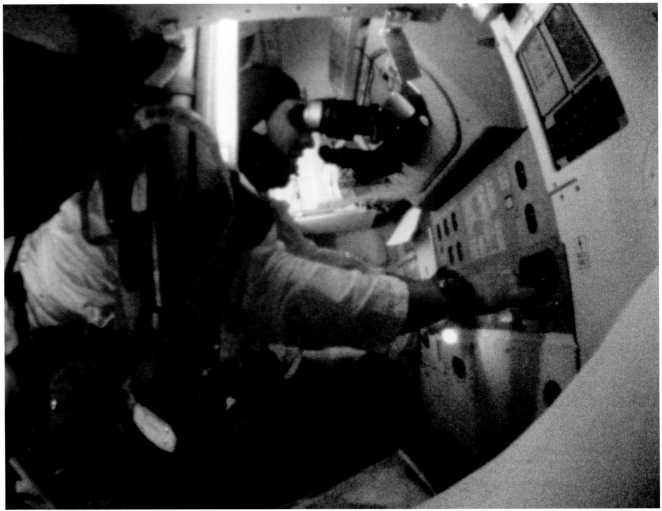

APOLLO
INNER, MIDDLE & OUTER GIMBAL ASSEMBLIES
IMU-5 FOR APOLLO G & N EQUIPMENT
apollo M.I.T. INSTRUMENTATION LABORATORY   AUGUST 1963

Above: *The Inertial Measurement Unit (IMU) consisted of a stable platform onto which were mounted three orthogonally displaced gyroscopes capable of measuring torque in pitch, roll and yaw. Signals from the IMU would be integrated with accelerometers to provide the crew and the Apollo Guidance Computer with information on the pointing angle of the spacecraft.*

Opposite above: *The Navigation Base was the rigid structure on the side wall of the Command Module, providing a mounting for the Apollo Guidance Computer, the optical assembly consisting of sextant and telescope, the Inertial Measurement Unit, and the display and keyboard assembly into which the operator input measurements.*

Opposite below: *A fuzzy still from an on-board TV transmission showing Jim Lovell at the optical instruments taking navigation sightings for backup data and for demonstrating how accurate the crew could be in obtaining position information, should they lose contact with Earth.*

whole assembly weighed 42.5lb (19.3kg) in a spherical case 12.6in (32cm) in diameter.

Finding their own way in space was not the preferred way of flying to the Moon and back, but it might have been essential if communication with the ground was lost. To give the crew navigation sightings, the spacecraft had a sextant and a telescope built in to the Command Module on the wall opposite the three couches, with the optics protruding through the hull. The electro-optical, dual line-of-sight sextant had a 28× magnification and a 1.8° field of view with the capacity to measure the included angle between any two targets to an accuracy of 10 arc-seconds, which is 0.00277 of a degree – one degree being $\frac{1}{360}$ of a full circle.

One line of sight would be established by changing the pointing angle of the spacecraft using a hand controller at the side of the optical instruments. The astronaut playing the role of navigator would operate the attitude control thrusters with a hand controller identical to that attached to the arm of the couch for attitude control. In effect, the operator would take over control of roll, pitch or yaw to optically acquire the target. The other line of sight would be aligned on the shaft and trunnion axes.

The single-line-of-sight refracting telescope was similar to a theodolite in that it could measure elevation and azimuth to a single target from an established reference. Again, shaft and trunnion angles would be used for reference to the attitude of the spacecraft.

The digital computer would store and use signals from the guidance platform and sighting angles from the optical assembly to calculate course corrections. With a fixed memory accommodating 38,864 words and an erasable memory containing up to 2,048 words, the computer provided all the information necessary to fly to the Moon and back. It was connected to two display keyboards, one on the wall adjacent to the optical assembly and a second on the main display console in front of the couches. Each contained ten numerical keys labelled 0 to 9, two key signs (+ and -) and seven keys for inserting instructions into the computer: Verb, Noun, Clear, Enter, Proceed, Key Release and Reset.

Numerical data would be fed to the computer via the Verb key, designating the action to be taken, and the Noun key, informing what that action was to be applied to, while the + and - signs indicated decimal values. The Clear key removed data from the displays, successive depressions continuing to clear the other addresses. The Proceed key would instruct the computer to hold on standby, or if already on standby to go ahead with normal operations. The Key Release function would wipe the illuminated display of the last entered numbers and show information from the computer programme. The Enter key told the computer to accept the numerical instructions, and Reset would clear the address.

CHAPTER 7

OUT OF THIS WORLD

As the flight of Apollo 8 progressed, the Earth continued to pull on the spacecraft, and by a mission elapsed time of 55hr 38min 40sec it had slowed to a mere 2,223mph (3,578km/h), at which point it entered the gravitational field of the Moon. At 202,540 miles (326,454km) from Earth, there were still 38,900 miles (62,598km) to go.

From this point the spacecraft would begin to speed up, gradually at first, reaching 5,720mph (9,2005km/h) at the time the SPS engine fired on the far side of the Moon, dropping it into lunar orbit. If that burn did not take place for some reason, Apollo 8 would loop around the Moon, whose gravitational attraction would act like a slingshot to throw the spacecraft on to an Earth-return trajectory: a free return ticket.

Getting into lunar orbit was a big moment for Apollo 8. Once committed, there was no way back home except with another burn using the same engine. The all-important Lunar Orbit Insertion (LOI) burn was to take place around the far side of the Moon at a height of 87 miles (140km) and an elapsed time of 69hr 8min 20sec, just 9min 35sec after disappearing around the left-hand side of the Moon as viewed from Earth. Shortly before losing contact with Houston, Bill Anders responded to a final call from Houston with a cheery "Thanks a lot, troops."

Above: *One of the most famous pictures of the 20th century – Earthrise from the Apollo 8 spacecraft coming round the Moon and into view of 3.5 billion people on what all the crew called "home".*

Opposite: *Human eyes had not seen the Moon this close until the flight of Apollo 8, although most of the views of the whole sphere would be taken by the crew after they left lunar orbit.*

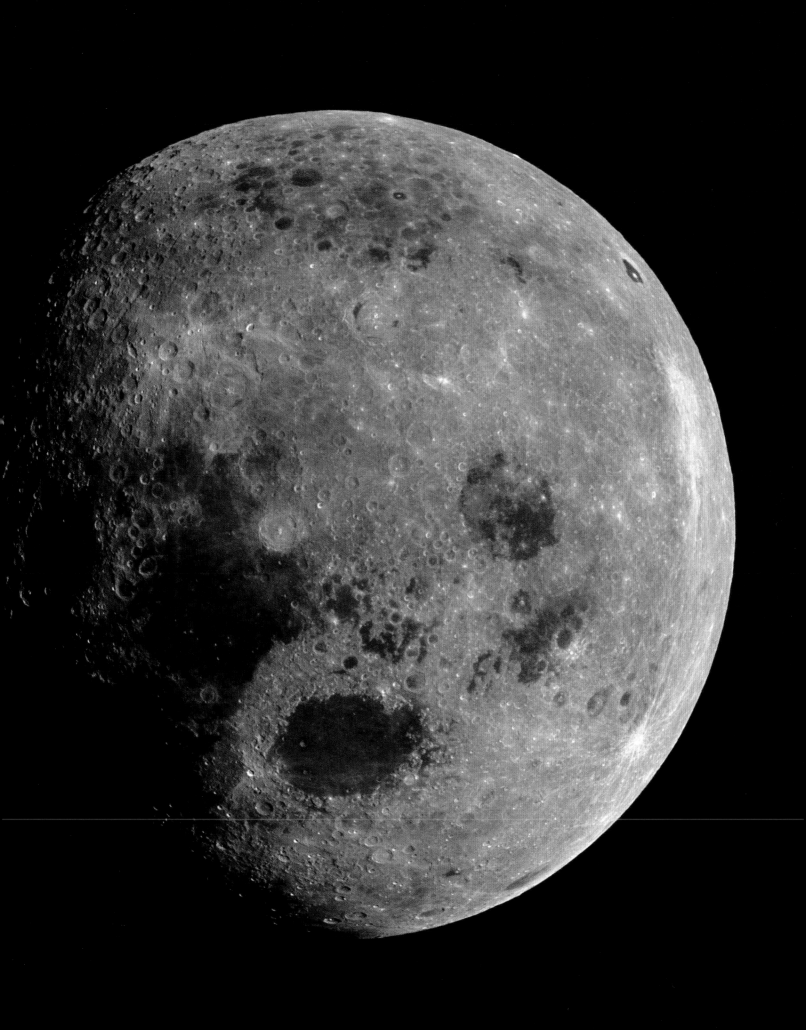

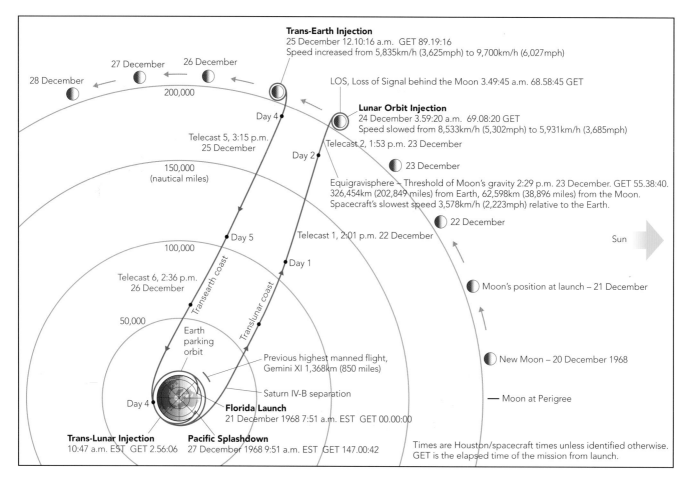

Trans-Earth Injection
25 December 12.10:16 a.m. GET 89.19:16
Speed increased from 5,835km/h (3,625mph) to 9,700km/h (6,027mph)

LOS, Loss of Signal behind the Moon 3.49:45 a.m. 68.58:45 GET

Lunar Orbit Injection
24 December 3.59:20 a.m. 69.08:20 GET
Speed slowed from 8,533km/h (5,302mph) to 5,931km/h (3,685mph)

Telecast 2, 1:53 p.m. 23 December

Equigravisphere – Threshold of Moon's gravity 2:29 p.m. 23 December. GET 55.38:40.
326,454km (202,849 miles) from Earth, 62,598km (38,896 miles) from the Moon.
Spacecraft's slowest speed 3,578km/h (2,223mph) relative to the Earth.

27 December   26 December
28 December
200,000

Day 4

Telecast 5, 3:15 p.m.
25 December

150,000
(nautical miles)

Day 2

23 December

22 December

Telecast 1, 2:01 p.m. 22 December

Sun

100,000

Day 5

Day 1

Telecast 6, 2:36 p.m.
26 December

Moon's position at launch – 21 December

50,000

Earth
parking
orbit

Transearth coast

Translunar coast

New Moon – 20 December 1968

Day 4

Previous highest manned flight,
Gemini XI 1,368km (850 miles)

Saturn IV-B separation

— Moon at Perigree

Florida Launch
21 December 1968 7:51 a.m. EST GET 00.00:00

Trans-Lunar Injection   **Pacific Splashdown**
10:47 a.m. EST GET 2.56:06   27 December 1968 9:51 a.m. EST GET 147.00:42

Times are Houston/spacecraft times unless identified otherwise.
GET is the elapsed time of the mission from launch.

If the burn had not taken place, the crew would appear around the right-hand side of the Moon (called the "limb") 10 minutes earlier than expected, indicating they had failed to fire the SPS engine and slow down. If the SPS had ignited and failed to shut down, they would slow too much and crash into the surface. It was a knife edge, with all eyes and ears at Mission Control waiting to see if the tracking stations would acquire data and voice contact at the earlier time.

There were two clocks on the wall – one counting down to the time the spacecraft would appear if the burn had not taken place, a second counting down to the target time if a successful burn had been achieved. The first clock reached zero and stopped – the spacecraft had not appeared, so some sort of burn had to have taken place.

IN THE GRIP OF THE MOON

For 35 minutes, for the first time, three humans were isolated from the (then) 3.5 billion people on Earth, totally alone and out of reach around the far side of the Moon, whose surface, because of the lighting angle, was primarily in sunlight. Then, at the expected time, the spacecraft appeared, data began to flow down to Mission Control indicating the planned SPS firing had occurred and at 69hr 34min 25sec, in response to a call from Houston, came the voice of Frank Borman confirming a successful burn: "Roger, Houston. We read you loud and clear."

The SPS engine had fired for 4min 6.9sec. Within minutes, Mission Control had verified that, having cut its speed by 2,043mph (3,287km/h), Apollo 8 was

Above: *A graphic depiction of key events in the flight of Apollo 8 showing the relative movement of the Moon.*

in a safe orbit of 69 × 194 miles (111 × 312km). It would take the spacecraft about two hours to make a complete circumnavigation of the Moon and on the second pass, on the far side, the SPS engine fired again to nearly circularize the orbit at 69 × 70 miles (111 × 113km).

Apollo 8 had slipped into lunar orbit in the early hours of Christmas Eve – in America it was still the hours before dawn, while in Europe it was late morning and in East Asia it was late afternoon. Throughout these momentous events, public affairs officer Paul Haney had struggled to convey in words the meaning of this day. For the crew, it meant a meal and some rest before the first TV transmission showing the dark, seemingly colourless face of the Moon, close-up and broadcast live for the first time by a handheld camera, those signals being picked up by the deep-space tracking station in Madrid, Spain, one of three around the globe.

The picture was not good; yet, in some ethereal way, it served to emphasize the far-out frontier along which humans were now walking. Set in the context of a nation in turmoil from race riots, an escalating war in Vietnam and the assassination of Martin Luther King and Bobby Kennedy, it offered a glimpse of a grander vision conjured by science, technology and the bold use of human ingenuity and design for exploration, discovery and invention.

For the Apollo 8 astronauts and a watching public preparing to celebrate one of the biggest religious festivals on Earth, it shone a light of hope that humans were, after all, capable of great things, of inspiring the young and creating a cohesive and united world, and that the malevolent inhumanity on a war-torn planet was an aberration rather than the norm. And from around another world in space, Apollo 8 prepared to send one last telecast. It was early evening in Houston, time for the evening office party in Washington, but in London and other European cities it was already Christmas Day; on both continents night had fallen.

From a makeshift studio at the Manned Spacecraft Center, correspondent Ed Hickey waited with his listeners for live views showing the Moon's dusty surface: "On the earlier transmission today, the Apollo 8 astronauts said the old Moon looked sort of greyish, sandy, very little colour, that there appeared to be craters which had been impacted by meteorites…. They are putting in a call down here from Mission Control, we're standing by waiting to hear from them…. And it seems impossible as we sit here and await this, and the earlier pictures we have seen, how anyone who can sit and watch their television monitor, as they are perhaps around the world, and not wonder, at what Man has wrought on this Christmas Day…."

What would be the final TV transmission from lunar orbit began around 8.35 p.m. on Christmas Eve, Houston time, with the astronauts describing the barren scene below, each reflecting on what the Moon looked like so very close.

Frank Borman believed that it "was a different thing to each one of us… each one carried his own impression of what he's seen today. I know my own impression is that it's a vast, lonely, forbidding type existence, or expanse of nothing. It looks rather like clouds of pumice stone."

Jim Lovell responded: "… my thoughts are very similar; the vast loneliness up here at the Moon is awe-inspiring and it makes you realize what you have back there on Earth. The Earth from here is a grand oasis in the big vastness of space."

After further discussion of the craters and the rilles, the mountains and the valleys, the crew had a very determined impression they wished to impart

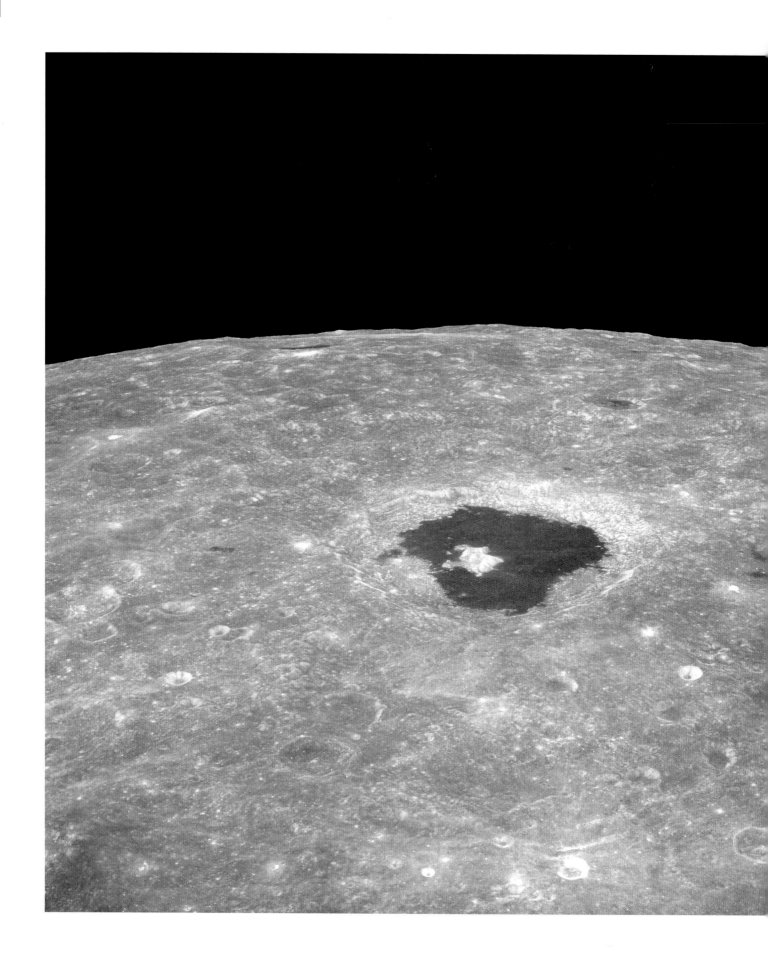

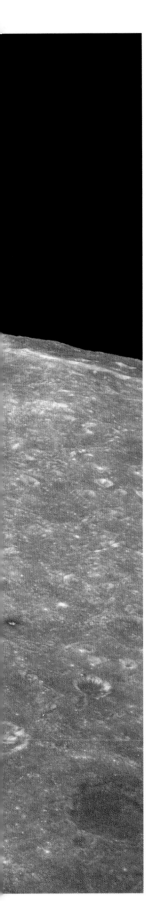

Above: *An oblique view from the Apollo 8 spacecraft looking eastwards across the far side of the lunar surface. The crater Tsiolkovsky in the centre of the picture is 93 miles (150km) wide and located at 129°E and 21°S. While in lunar orbit, Apollo 8 moved towards the camera position over the terrain along the left (north) side of this photograph.*

Left: *This oblique view of the lunar surface was taken from the Apollo 8 spacecraft looking southward towards Goclenius and other large craters near 45°E and 10°S in the Sea of Fertility. Goclenius, the crater in the foreground with a rille-broken flat floor, is about 45 miles (70km) in diameter. The two large craters with smooth floors are Colombo A (left) and Magelhaens. Magelhaens A, the crater with the irregular floor, is about 20 miles (35km) in diameter.*

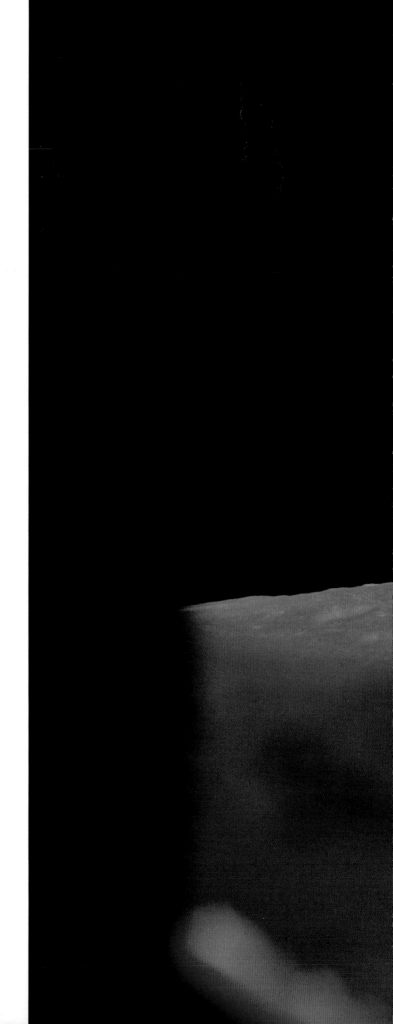

Right: *High-oblique view of the Moon's surface showing Earth rising above the lunar horizon, looking west-south-west. The centre of the picture is located at about 105°E and 13°S. The lunar surface has less pronounced colour than indicated here.*

in the closing minutes of the final telecast from Moon orbit, a special and carefully considered message to all people of many different faiths, beliefs and philosophies across the world on that Christmas night. It was close to 9.00 p.m. in Houston, 3.00 a.m. in London and 5.00 a.m. in Moscow when Bill Anders began to present a Christmas message in which all three astronauts would participate:

"We are now approaching lunar sunrise (actually sunset) and for all the people back on Earth, the crew of Apollo 8 has a message that we would like to send to you," and he began reading the first four versus from Genesis Chapter 1: "In the beginning, God created the heaven and the Earth. And the Earth was without form and void; and darkness was upon the face of the deep. And the Spirit of God moved upon the face of the waters. And God said let there be light and there was light. And God saw the light, that it was good. And God divided the light from the darkness."

Jim Lovell took up the following four versus before Frank Borman read the next two, ending by imparting a very personal message: "And from the crew of Apollo 8, we close with goodnight, good luck, a merry Christmas, and God Bless all of you – all of you on the Good Earth." The Good Earth had been used as a metaphor, stimulated by the book of that name written by Pearl S. Buck in 1931 about a poor, Chinese farm boy who believed that by working the land, applying effort and living in harmony with nature the individual finds the basis of happiness and fulfilment – at one with the Good Earth.

THERE IS A SANTA CLAUS

after ten revolutions of the Moon it was time to come home. At 89hr 19min 16sec on the far side of the Moon the SPS engine fired again, this time for 3min 23.7sec, adding 2,400mph (3,862km/h) to its speed and shooting Apollo 8 out of lunar orbit and on its way back to Earth. This time it was the tracking station in Australia that was locked on to the signal of the spacecraft when it reappeared around the eastern limb of the Moon as viewed from Earth. In Houston, it was the first hour of Christmas Day and at 12.25 a.m. Jim Lovell called down and confirmed what every child already knew: "Please be informed, there is a Santa Claus!"

Apollo 8 sailed back into communication, and in Mission Control the chart of the Moon used for the last day in plotting the progress of the spacecraft suddenly switched to a map of Earth, and a moving indicator showing the spot, deep in space, over which the vehicle was passing – the sub-spacecraft location. To make the tired and overworked flight control team just that little bit more responsive to what day it was around the world, somebody had wheeled in a big Christmas tree and set it up, lights twinkling from the moment Apollo 8 reappeared.

For Borman, Lovell and Anders, the sudden awareness of how tense they had been, how hard they had worked during the 20 hours spent orbiting the Moon, became all too present. Nevertheless, for them there were more navigation sightings, snatched sleep periods, meals and engineering tests filling the balance of Christmas Day. And soon they would be setting up the barbecue-roll of passive thermal control as the spacecraft gradually rotated about its long axis.

Next day brought another TV show from the returning spacecraft, with more homespun philosophy from a crew that had truly been to the edge of human experience. To Bill Anders, the return home prompted a reflection: "I think I must have the feeling that the travellers in the old sailing ships must have [had], going on a very long voyage away from home and now we're heading back and I have this feeling of being proud of the trip but still happy to be going back home and back to our home port."

As with the outbound journey, Apollo 8 on its return slipped through the point where the Earth's pull once again became dominant and the ever-present gravitational attraction of the Moon was exchanged with that of the home planet. That point came at 100hr 47min 47sec when the spacecraft was 38,920 miles (62,622km) from the Moon and 201,998 miles (325,015km) from Earth, its speed diminished by lunar gravity to a mere 4,725mph (7,603km/h) at the crossover point.

Tracking data verified that the Trans-Earth Injection (TEI) burn had indeed been precise and the only "tweak" of the flight path came at an elapsed time of 103hr 59min 54sec, adjusting the velocity of the spacecraft by a mere 3.27mph (5.26km/h) while simultaneously adjusting the angle of the trajectory. It took only a squirt from the thrusters, the big SPS engine having already done its job.

Apollo 8's return to Earth took less than 58 hours, about eight hours faster than the outbound trip. Preparations for re-entry began during the early hours of 27 December, with all three crew members awake and conducting final systems checks before the fast-paced sequence of events that would see them splashing

Below: *An artist's depiction of the Apollo 8 Command Module slicing into the Earth's atmosphere, making a shallow dive before lifting to gain altitude and then dropping again to an even shallower ride down to the point where parachutes will deploy.*

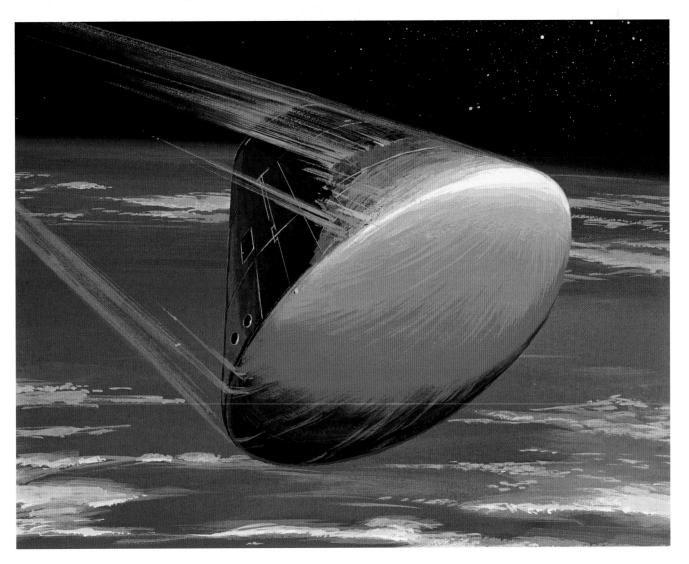

down in the mid-Pacific recovery zone at 9.51 a.m. Houston time. Only the conical-shaped Command Module had a shield to protect it from the searing heat of re-entry, so the Service Module would be jettisoned about 17 minutes before hitting the atmosphere, following along behind the manned capsule and burning up before it hit the ocean.

The first significant step was to switch electrical power from the three fuel cells in the Service Module to on-board entry batteries in the Command Module and to reconfigure communications. Separation from the Service Module occurred on time at 146hr 28min 48sec, pyrotechnic squibs firing to sever the ties that had firmly connected the two modules throughout the mission. Entry interface occurred at 146hr 46min 13sec with the Command Module streaking into the outer atmosphere at a speed of 24,695mph (39,735km/h) and an altitude of 75.76 miles (121.92km).

The altitude at which the atmosphere ends and the vacuum of space begins is an arbitrary number, marked for re-entry purposes as the height at which a

Below: *The crew of Apollo 8 arrives on the deck of the carrier USS Yorktown, to the relief of millions around the world watching on TV.*

returning spacecraft experiences a deceleration of 0.05g – one "g" being the pull of the Earth's gravitational field at the surface (32ft/sec^2 or 9.75m/sec^2) due to atmospheric pressure. At that point the Command Module was 1,553 miles (2,499km) up-range of the splashdown point, slicing into the atmosphere on a flight path at an angle of only 5.5°.

To relieve the heat shield from absorbing too much thermal energy too early, the descent path levelled out at a height of 36 miles (57.9km) and a range-to-go of 1,000 miles (1,600km). To achieve this, the computer controlled the pitch angle of the conical Command Module, changing the degree of lift it carried and initiating steering re-entry. After a modest lift, the spacecraft dipped back down to an altitude of 34.1 miles (54.8km) before raising the flight path back up again, this time to 38 miles (61km) high before beginning the final descent path some 345 miles (555km) from the splashdown point.

As the speed fell away through deceleration from the increasingly dense atmosphere, the near-horizontal glide path gradually became a near-vertical descent and the parachute system took over. Each 16.5ft (5m) in diameter, two drogue-parachutes were deployed at 24,000ft (7,315m), slowing the spacecraft from 300mph (483km/h) to 175mph (281km/h). At 10,000ft (3,048m), the drogues were released, pulling out three pilot parachutes which in turn extracted three main parachutes. With a full inflated diameter of 83.5ft (25.4m), these were initially deployed in the reefed, or partially deployed, configuration to reduce the sudden jolt of their inflation.

At full inflation, the main parachutes slowed the Command Module to a speed of 22mph (35km/h), at which speed the spacecraft sliced into the waters

Above: *From left to right, Borman, Anders and Lovell find it hard to suppress their enthusiasm for their mission, a vital step on the path to the first manned landing on the lunar surface.*

at splashdown in the Pacific Ocean at an elapsed time of 147hr 00min 42sec. To prevent the base of the Command Module pancaking into the water with a bone-bruising shock, it was suspended from the parachutes at an angle of 27.5° so that it would go in toe-first and slide to a stable position. But that could be either right side up (Stable I) or upside down. Dragged over to an inverted position by the swell of the ocean (Stable II), Apollo 8's Command Module was restored to Stable I by flipping it over using three air bags in its forward section, each inflating to a volume of 22cu ft (0.62cu m).

Apollo 8 landed in the Pacific Ocean just before dawn, on a line of latitude about 1,000 miles (1,609km) south-south-west of Honolulu. The recovery forces waited until daylight to start their operations, which began when the

Above: *The Apollo Command Module was recovered from the Pacific Ocean, and is now on display for visitors to see at the Chicago Museum of Science and Industry.*

first slivers of light appeared, 44 minutes after splashdown. The seas were relatively calm, waves at 6ft (1.8m), the water a comfortable 82°F (28°C) and winds light – close to ideal conditions. The carrier USS *Yorktown* deployed swimmers and the hatch was opened at 11.03a.m. Houston time, some 72 minutes after splashdown. Just over an hour later, the *Yorktown* was close by the spacecraft, which was hoisted aboard at 12.20 p.m. Houston time.

Above: *The crew share a joke during debriefings back at the Manned Spacecraft Center, where the decision was made to proceed with two more rehearsals before attempting the first landing.*

Right: *Newsweek magazine devotes the cover and considerable interior content for the first issue in 1969 to the magnificent success of one of NASA's most audacious missions.*

CHAPTER 8

ROADS TO THE MOON

Having demonstrated on Apollos 7 and 8 that the Command and Service Modules were fit for lunar voyages, it was now time for NASA to pick up the pace with the much-delayed Lunar Module (LM). This was a complex spacecraft. Carried for launch inside the void created by the protective panels that supported the Apollo spacecraft on top of the Saturn V, it was not designed to return to Earth. Once separated from the mother ship, the astronauts had to get back to the Apollo capsule to return home.

The first flight of LM-1, the first production model, had demonstrated that the basic systems could operate in space despite some technical problems during that flight (Apollo 5) in January 1968. But chasing down the quality-control criteria proved difficult with such complex and demanding technology, where reliability was key to survival of the crew. So it was that the Moon-orbiting flight of Apollo 8 preceded that of the first flight of the combined Apollo and Lunar Module, which was held back by difficulties and time-consuming workaround procedures.

This delayed the first manned checkout flight of the LM until 3 March 1969, when astronauts Jim McDivitt, Dave Scott and Russell "Rusty" Schweickart were launched aboard Apollo 9 on a purely Earth-orbiting flight lasting just over 10 days. This was the first time both the Apollo spacecraft and the Lunar Module were launched together as they would be for a landing mission. They were each given identification names as call signs to Mission Control: the Apollo spacecraft was Gumdrop (after the sweet) and the LM known as Spider (because of its spidery legs).

Many tests were conducted during the Apollo 9 mission, including the various systems of the LM guidance and

Opposite: *A view from the Apollo mother ship as the crew look down on the Lunar Module, still firmly in the embrace of the adapter on top of the Saturn V S-IVB stage that had delivered them to orbit.*

Below: *The crew for Apollo 9 (left to right): Commander Jim McDivitt, Command Module Pilot Dave Scott; Lunar Module Pilot Russell "Rusty" Schweickart. The flight would demonstrate that the Lunar Module could be taken to the Moon for a final dress rehearsal before the landing attempt.*

navigation equipment. Just as Apollo astronauts had to be capable of guiding their spacecraft back to Earth should communications with Mission Control be lost, so too had the LM pilots to be capable of finding the mother ship should they suffer a similar loss of communications. There was also a need to check the two separate guidance systems – one for the normal prosecution of the mission and an abort system that would take over if the primary system failed for some reason.

Because the LM consisted of two sections – the Descent Stage and the Ascent Stage – it was vital that the two should be tested with astronauts on board and a wide range of engine tests conducted to demonstrate all manner of operational and potential contingency firings that might be called upon on later flights. McDivitt and Schweickart entered Spider on the second day of the mission and thoroughly checked its systems before firing the descent engine for nearly 6min 10sec. This was the only time the descent engine was fired on a scheduled exercise while the Lunar Module was docked to Apollo; on Apollo 13 it would be used when the LM on that mission served as a lifeboat to steer the crew home from a near-disastrous explosion.

Three days into the mission, Schweickart entered the LM through the docking tunnel, donned a space suit and opened the forward hatch which, on a landing flight, would be used to go down the ladder to the surface of the Moon. On this flight he was scheduled to make his way across to the Apollo Command Module using external handrails, demonstrating that an astronaut could use that method to reach the mother ship should the docking tunnel be blocked or damaged. While Dave Scott stood in the open Apollo hatch, Schweickart successfully showed that the LM hatch could be opened in a vacuum but failed to transfer across as planned, due to the after-effects of space sickness, similar to motion sickness.

Almost four days into the Earth-orbit mission came the moment for McDivitt and Schweickart to take the LM and fly it away to demonstrate that it was indeed an independent spacecraft, and to test some of the manoeuvres necessary for a landing mission. For the first time, at 92hr 39min, the crewed LM separated from the Apollo spacecraft.

After drifting apart for half of one orbit, during which time the radar and guidance platform was checked, the descent engine was fired for just under 19 seconds under the command of the abort computer. This positioned the LM some 11.5 miles (18.5km) above and 31 miles (50km) behind Apollo, at which distance the descent engine fired again, this time for 22 seconds using the primary computer, taking Spider further behind Gumdrop to a maximum distance of 86 miles (138km).

At this point, at an elapsed time of 96hr 16min, the Ascent Stage separated from the Descent Stage and a manoeuvre from the thrusters set up the orbit for a rendezvous with the mother ship from a distance of 90 miles (145km). Now exposed, the ascent engine fired for the

Below: *The docking probe was attached to the forward apex end of the Command Module and is shown here extended, with a cone-shaped device that would be inserted into a receptacle on the drogue on the top of the Lunar Module. When latched, the probe would be retracted, securely pulling the two together with 24 latches around the periphery of what became the docking tunnel after the probe was removed and stowed.*

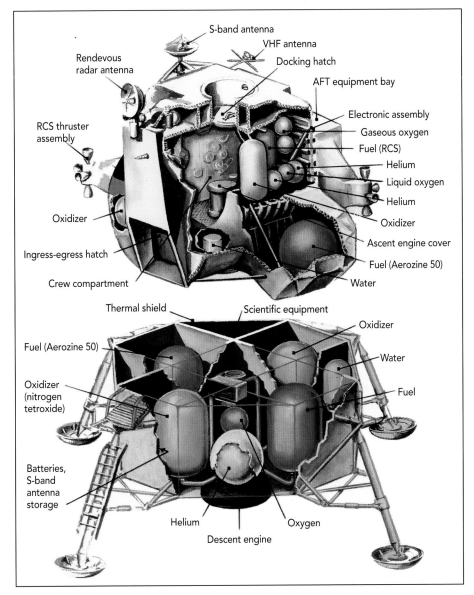

S-band antenna

VHF antenna

Rendevous
radar antenna

Docking hatch

AFT equipment bay

RCS thruster
assembly

Electronic assembly

Gaseous oxygen

Fuel (RCS)

Helium

Liquid oxygen

Helium

Oxidizer

Oxidizer

Ascent engine cover

Ingress-egress hatch

Fuel (Aerozine 50)

Crew compartment

Water

Thermal shield

Scientific equipment

Oxidizer

Fuel (Aerozine 50)

Water

Oxidizer
(nitrogen
tetroxide)

Fuel

Batteries,
S-band
antenna
storage

Helium

Oxygen

Descent engine

Left: *The two elements of the Lunar Module. The pressurized Ascent Stage on top carried the two-man crew while the Descent Stage carried the rocket motor and its propellant used for descending to the lunar surface. It was left on the lunar surface while the crew returned to the Apollo spacecraft in orbit.*

first time on this mission at 96hr 58min and verified its operation in a burn lasting 2.9 seconds. Rendezvous was completed, with a redocking achieved at 99hr 2min, after which McDivitt and Schweickart rejoined Scott in Gumdrop.

At 101hr 22min the Ascent Stage was cut loose. The ascent engine was commanded by Mission Control to fire to depletion of its propellants in a burn starting 20 minutes later and lasting 5min 50sec, simulating the duration of a burn bringing Moon walkers back from the lunar surface to the mother ship and obtaining valuable telemetry on its performance in space.

For more than five days the crew remained in orbit, initially resting from three days of intensive activity and then completing two more firings with the Service Module engine, taking scientific photographs of Earth and selected targets below while continuing to conduct engineering checks and systems evaluations. They finally returned to Earth after 10 days 1hr 00min 54sec, having ridden on the fourth Saturn V flight, flown the third manned Apollo spacecraft and evaluated the first manned Lunar Module, effectively clearing all hardware elements for a full dress rehearsal of the first manned landing on the Moon.

CHARLIE BROWN AND SNOOPY

The crew selected for Apollo 10 included two veterans and a rookie: Commander Tom Stafford had flown on Gemini VI-A and IX-A and Command Module Pilot John Young had flown Gemini III and X; Lunar Module Pilot Eugene Cernan was making his second flight after accompanying Stafford on Gemini IX-A. They faced an intensive series of tests and evaluations, of techniques and operating procedures that would involve both Apollo and the Lunar Module around the Moon for the first time. The crew would also conduct a photographic reconnaissance on the four candidate landing sites, taking the LM through all the flight events associated with a landing, short of going down to the surface.

Apollo 10 was launched on 18 May 1969, with spacecraft named after the Charles Schultz comic strip "Peanuts": the Lunar Module being called Snoopy, because it would be "snooping around" down close to the Moon's surface, and the Apollo spacecraft Charlie Brown. The same sequence of events followed closely those described for Apollo 8, as they had for Apollo 9, but unlike the preceding flight, and like Apollo 8, the S-IVB third stage of the giant Saturn V would fire a second time to send them out of Earth orbit and on to the Moon. But this time, unlike Apollo 8, the Apollo mother ship turned around and extracted Snoopy from on top of the inert stage.

It took just over three days to reach lunar orbit, the SPS engine having already been fired once on the way out to place the trajectory on a similar

Opposite: *The Apollo spacecraft and Lunar Module are locked together while Scott stands in the open hatch of the Command Module and Schweickart takes pictures. Note the handrail, which would assist an astronaut moving from one to the other should the docking tunnel connecting the two vehicles become unusable.*

Above: *The Ascent Stage of the Apollo 9 Lunar Module Spider, to which the Apollo spacecraft will soon dock at the end of several hours of testing in free flight.*

path to that which Apollo 11 would follow for the correct lighting angles at candidate site No. 2 – the one preferred by the science selection team for a safe touchdown. As with Apollo 8, the orbit was circularized to about 69 miles (111km). Before starting a rest period, Stafford and Cernan opened up the LM and checked its systems in preparation for the big events on the following day.

Almost exactly four days after launch, the two LM crew members entered Snoopy again and at an elapsed time of 98hr 12min they separated from Charlie Brown, leaving John Young alone in the Command Module. Just over 35 minutes later Charlie Brown fired its thrusters to push away from Snoopy, followed 69 minutes later with a firing of the Lunar Module's descent engine. This burn lasted 27 seconds but changed the LM's path to an elliptical orbit dropping it down as close as 9.6 miles (15.4km) from the surface at the low point, known as pericynthion.

This would be exactly the trajectory followed by the first landing crew, and the pathfinder role played by Snoopy on Apollo 10 provided precise data on the gravitational field of the Moon and how it acted on the orbits of both the Lunar Module and the Apollo spacecraft. Flying this precursor route also allowed for checking the accuracy of the landing radar which, even from the altitude flown by Snoopy, would reach the surface 9.3 miles (15km) below.

All these procedures would be part of a normal landing mission and allow both spacecraft and Mission Control to check systems and tracking equipment to verify that this technique would work. But in dropping down towards the lunar surface, Snoopy had speeded up and was now 185 miles (298km) ahead of and below the Apollo spacecraft. To simulate the arrival of the LM in lunar orbit after lifting off from the surface, Snoopy had to get far behind Charlie Brown and carry out rendezvous and docking procedures to demonstrate that these operations worked too.

To set up the trajectory for getting Snoopy behind Charlie Brown, the descent engine fired up again at 100hr 58min, this time for 40 seconds, changing velocity by 120mph (193km/h) and placing the spacecraft in a new elliptical orbit with a high point of 218 miles (350km). Just as falling closer to the Moon caused the LM to speed up, so the high looping path now taken by Snoopy slowed it down. When it came back down half an orbit later it was behind and below Charlie Brown, exactly as it would be had the LM been coming up from the lunar surface.

It took almost two hours for Snoopy to loop up and come back down, with less than ten minutes between two critical events. First the Descent Stage would be jettisoned, followed by the firing of the ascent engine to bring the high point of the elliptical orbit back down to below the orbit of Charlie Brown up ahead. Because it would then be on an inner track to Charlie Brown's orbit,

Above: *The Apollo 9 crew (left to right) of Schweickart, Scott and McDivitt, safely back on their recovery ship USS Guadalcanal in the Atlantic Ocean east of the Bahamas.*

Opposite below: *The crew selected for the full dress rehearsal for the Moon landing attempt consisted of (left to right) Eugene Cernan, Commander Tom Stafford and Command Module Pilot John Young. Cernan and Young would command the last two Apollo Moon missions (16 and 17) in 1972.*

it would start to catch up; as this orbit was gradually raised by further manoeuvres, it would slow down relative to the Apollo spacecraft until brought to a halt so that the two could dock together. But it didn't quite work out that way.

Staging took place at an elapsed time of 102hr 45min, but Cernan had left switches in an incorrect position and, although the event was controlled by the primary computer, the abort guidance system was also switched on. Believing that an emergency had occurred and that the Ascent Stage needed to go and find Charlie Brown immediately, it now took hold of the spacecraft's attitude and flung it around in a wild gyration, its radar searching for the mother ship. The astronauts took less than a couple of minutes to discover the cause, switch off the AGS and resume the planned sequence.

Ten minutes after staging, the ascent engine fired for 15 seconds, placing Snoopy in an orbit of 53.5 × 12.6 miles (86 × 20.3km), lower and about 400 miles (644km) behind Charlie Brown, exactly where it should be to chase down the mother ship. After several manoeuvres performed by the thrusters on Snoopy, the two spacecraft were reunited, with a docking at 106hr 22min, some 8hr 10min after separating.

It had been a long day but arguably the most important since December the previous year, when Apollo 8 proved that the Command and Service Modules

Above: *The Saturn V launch vehicle for Apollo 10 emerges from the rear of the Vehicle Assembly Building at the start of its journey to Launch Complex 39B, the second of two launch pads built for the giant Moon rocket. This was the inaugural use of that location (the previous four Saturn V launches having been from LC-39A).*

Above: *The view looking back at the Earth during the three-day coast to the Moon, showing the North American continent with Baja California clearly visible.*

could carry astronauts to the Moon and back – safely. Now it was known that the Lunar Module could do most tasks for which it was designed – the final and most demanding test being the actual landing on the Moon.

After Stafford and Cernan got back into Charlie Brown, about 13 hours after they had begun powering up the LM's systems at the start of this day's events, Snoopy's Ascent Stage was cut loose just over two hours after redocking, and ground controllers commanded its engine to fire until propellant depletion. Snoopy had carried much less propellant than for a landing mission and the burn lasted 3min 33sec, propelling the inert stage out of lunar orbit and into a path where it will perpetually orbit the Sun at the approximate distance of the Earth-Moon system.

Charlie Brown spent a further full Earth day in lunar orbit before the SPS engine was fired at 137hr 36min to bring them home, splashdown occurring at 192hr 3min – eight days in total since launch. The crew had performed beyond the expectations of those projecting NASA's stories to the public, transmitting 19 TV sessions for the public relations machine in contrast to the 11 planned, almost doubling the time viewers on Earth got to see live broadcasts from the spacecraft.

Below: *The Ascent Stage to Lunar Module Snoopy comes back to redock with Charlie Brown after demonstrating the full flight capabilities of the Moon lander.*

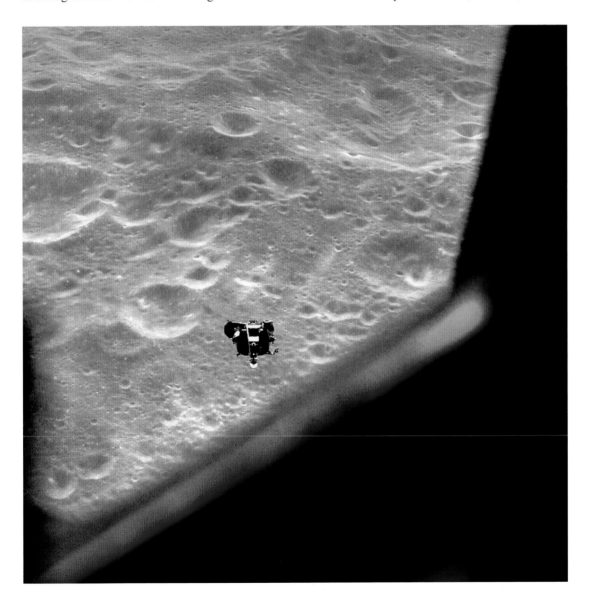

TAXI FOR TWO

The Lunar Module consisted of the unpressurized Descent Stage and the Ascent Stage, which contained the pressurized crew compartment. These remained attached until the time came to use the Descent Stage as a launch pad for the Ascent Stage to carry the crew back from the lunar surface to the mother ship in orbit about the Moon.

The primary function of the Descent Stage was to contain the four propellant tanks for the main engine used to lower the spacecraft down to the Moon after it separated from Apollo in lunar orbit. This engine could be throttled up and down between set ranges so that it could balance the diminishing weight of the spacecraft as it consumed propellant against the need to progressively reduce the descent velocity and come to a hover, gently controlling the final phase of touchdown. The descent engine had a maximum thrust of 9,870lb (44.9kN) and consumed nitrogen tetroxide and Aerozene-50, the latter a blend of two different compounds of hydrazine.

The Ascent Stage provided a pressurized volume for two astronauts, four thruster quads for controlling the attitude of the Lunar Module throughout flight, plus an ascent engine for launch from the Descent Stage to achieve lunar orbit insertion for a rendezvous with the Apollo spacecraft. Using the same propellants as the descent engine, it had a fixed thrust of 3,500lb (15.57kN) and could also be used

to abort the landing and fire off from the Descent Stage should something go wrong on the way down.

Because the Lunar Module was designed to operate for a nominal 72 hours, compared with 240 hours for the mother ship, electrical power could be provided by six batteries, of which four were in the Descent Stage and two in the Ascent Stage. This saved weight over the fuel cells and cryogenic hydrogen and oxygen reactants carried in the Apollo Service Module. The quantity of oxygen carried had to take account of the cycle of depressurizing, whereby all the oxygen was vented to the vacuum of space for getting out on the Moon, and then repressurizing the crew cabin with more oxygen from the tank in the Descent Stage after they got back in.

The systems and technologies adopted for the Lunar Module were distinctly different from those in the Apollo spacecraft because the two had been designed by different companies, with starting points almost two years apart. When it separated from the Apollo spacecraft, the Lunar Module had an average weight of 33,500lb (15,196kg), of which almost two-thirds was the weight of the Descent Stage and the 18,300lb (8,300kg) propellants it carried for the descent engine. On its own, the Ascent Stage weighed around 10,500lb (4,763kg), of which 5,861lb (2,658kg) was propellant for the ascent engine.

Opposite: *The Lunar Module, legs folded in, is hoisted into position. With legs extended, it provides a means of getting down to the surface from the square-shaped hatch at the front centre of the Ascent Stage. At the top front is the rendezvous radar.*

Right: *The Lunar Module Descent Stage consisted of a box cruciform structure supporting the four propellant tanks for the main descent engine. It also provided consumables and electrical power from batteries to support the two men during their stay on the surface.*

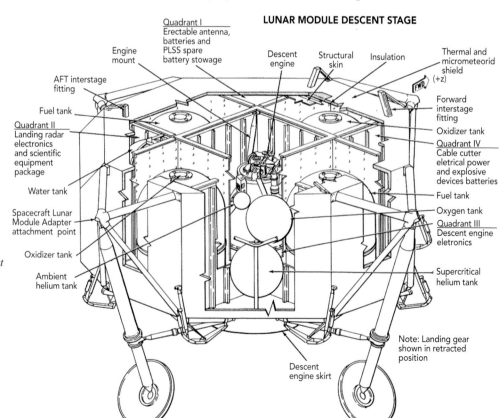

LUNAR MODULE DESCENT STAGE

Quadrant I
Erectable antenna, batteries and PLSS spare battery stowage

Engine mount

AFT interstage fitting

Fuel tank

Quadrant II
Landing radar electronics and scientific equipment package

Water tank

Spacecraft Lunar Module Adapter attachment point

Oxidizer tank

Ambient helium tank

Descent engine

Structural skin

Insulation

Thermal and micrometeorid shield (+z)

FWD

Forward interstage fitting

Oxidizer tank

Quadrant IV
Cable cutter eletrical power and explosive devices batteries

Fuel tank

Oxygen tank

Quadrant III
Descent engine eletronics

Supercritical helium tank

Descent engine skirt

Note: Landing gear shown in retracted position

CHAPTER 9

THE EAGLE HAS LANDED

"One small step for man..."

The triumphant return of the Apollo 10 crew punctuated the finale on pre-landing preparation flights and cleared the path for Apollo 11 to be the first attempt at going all the way to the surface of the Moon and back. In Owen Maynard's alphabet of steps, this was the first "G" mission – an engineering flight to demonstrate that the technology could fulfil the goal of landing on the Moon before the end of the decade, while verifying the procedures defined by the hardware.

The Apollo 11 mission was to be crewed by Neil Armstrong as Commander (CDR), Jim Lovell as Command Module Pilot (CMP) and Edwin "Buzz" Aldrin as Lunar Module Pilot (LMP). But that was changed when Mike Collins replaced Lovell following a successful bone-spur operation that had sidelined him until his recovery promised an early slot on his return to the flight roster. As a result, Lovell would command the backup crew, with William Anders as CMP and Fred Haise as LMP, and recycle for the command of Apollo 13.

WITH ALL OF HUMANITY

To avoid the flippancy of the earlier mission, NASA's Assistant Director of Public Affairs Julian Scheer wrote to Apollo Manager George Low to temper the frivolous use of spacecraft names. For this very historic flight, the Apollo spacecraft would be called Columbia, representing the United States and passing a nod to the 1865 novel from Jules Verne in which a projectile named Columbiad had been fired to the Moon from a giant cannon. The Lunar Module would carry the call sign Eagle, the national bird of the United States.

Mike Collins designed the mission motif, showing an eagle landing with an olive branch in its talons – a personal message of peace, which carried forward to the plaque riveted to Eagle's forward landing leg bearing the message "Here men from the planet Earth first set foot upon the Moon – We came in peace for all mankind", along with the signatures of all three crew members and Richard Nixon as President at the time the event occurred (but no reference to John F. Kennedy who had, albeit with doubts, initiated the programme).

The Rev. Ralph Abernathy, spiritual successor to Dr Martin Luther King, led 25 poor families from the south to a gate at the Kennedy Space

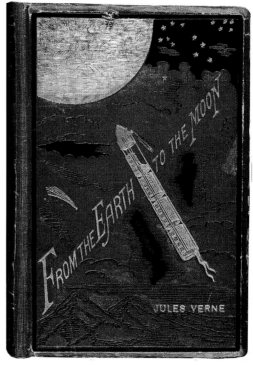

Below: *Prophetically, Jules Verne's From the Earth to the Moon foretold of a flight to Earth's nearest celestial neighbour in a projectile fired by a gun named Columbiad, recognized when the crew chose Columbia for the name of the Command and Service Modules.*

Above: *Commander Neil Armstrong (left) was a civilian astronaut who had made his name as a test pilot, flying the hypersonic rocket-propelled research aircraft X-15 and the Gemini XIII spacecraft. Command Module Pilot Mike Collins (centre) had flown on the Gemini X mission. The Lunar Module Pilot, Edwin "Buzz" Aldrin (right), had written a thesis on spacecraft rendezvous for his PhD and had previously flown on the Gemini XII mission. None would fly a third time.*

Right: *The basic design of the Apollo 11 mission badge was sketched out by Mike Collins, with the American eagle carrying an olive branch in its talons. As Collins explained, "We wanted to keep our three names off it because we wanted the design to be representative of everyone who had worked toward a lunar landing, and there were thousands who could take a proprietary interest in it, yet who would never see their names woven into the fabric of a patch. Further, we wanted the design to be symbolic rather than explicit."*

Center where they hoped to watch the launch. NASA Administrator Tom Paine went down to the gate and heard their plea for more attention to the poverty-stricken, asserting that "it will be a lot harder to solve the problems of hunger and poverty than it is to send men to the Moon"; he opened the gate and ushered them to the VIP stand where, when the launch came, Ralph Abernathy wept in awe at the unfolding drama.

From everywhere people came, flying in by helicopter and fixed-wing aircraft, driving in aboard plush limousines, walking from endless traffic jams. On the day before launch the intensity of preparations reached a crescendo matched only by the flood of humanity that arrived outside the Kennedy Space Center. Almost all were ordered and disciplined, many visibly moved

Above: *Neil Armstrong, Mike Collins and Buzz Aldrin leave the Manned Spacecraft Operations Building on the morning of 16 July 1969 for a ride in the transfer van to Launch Complex 39A, from where they would depart for the Moon.*

as though the event they were about to witness was worth endless privations, an event of almost spiritual significance.

In the air hundreds of aircraft flew over Brevard County and at sea thousands of tiny boats pitched and tossed on the Atlantic swell as cutters and Coast Guard vessels tried almost in vain to keep them from the abort recovery areas. It was hot that July, the air hanging like wet velvet across the dense congregations, but by the evening before launch more than 500,000 people were on the beaches, along the sandy strips and by the roadsides. Nobody had ever seen anything like it before and the intense enthusiasm evident among the spectators belied the polls, which said that more Americans approved a halt to space activity than thought it should continue.

Across the nation, retailers reported a surge in sales of colour TV sets, radios, toys related to space themes and models of Snoopy and Charlie Brown, the beloved mascots of the Apollo 10 pathfinder. Perhaps more significant than anything else was the statistic that in the months preceding this day, the death rate dropped dramatically as a euphoria set in, culminating in this one flight. Within weeks of the mission's end, the rate would be back to normal.

Inside the NASA monastery the pressure had been palpably intense, with a strong sense of responsibility from the lowest-paid worker to the highest official in the organization, driving a permeating sense of concern that each one had done his utmost to ensure success and the safe return of the crew. Emotional ties to the mission were equally intense and challenged the clinical restraint demanded by a complex and lofty objective.

Below: *The configuration of the Personal Life Support System backpack used by each crewmember, providing oxygen, communications, thermal control and electrical power for the pumps and bioharness attached to the astronaut's body.*

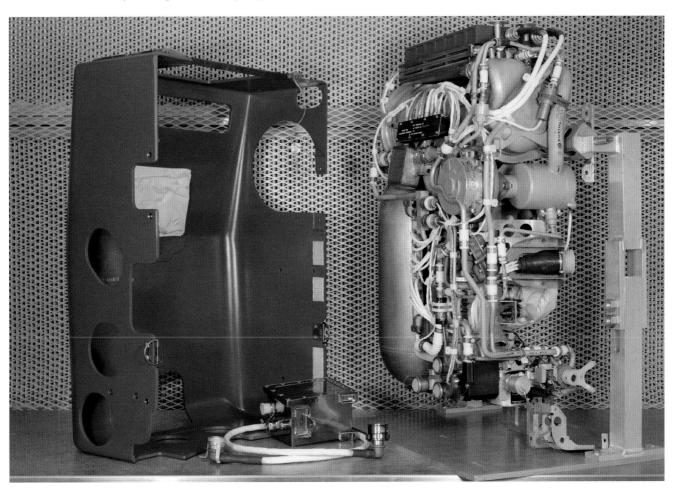

THE LONG RIDE

The launch was planned for 16 July 1969, a date selected so that the Sun angle casting shadows across the landing site at the time of lunar touchdown was at an elevation of about 10.8° from behind the Lunar Module. This was a compromise between a high angle, when the bright Sun across the airless Moon would wash out the view, and a low angle, which would provide insufficient light on the view ahead. Constraints for abort landings in daylight and the disposition of tracking stations around the Earth meant that the "window" for 16 July began at 9.32 a.m. local time and lasted 4hr 22sec.

Armstrong, Collins and Aldrin were woken at 4.15 a.m. local time at Cape Canaveral to breakfast on orange juice, steak, scrambled eggs, toast and coffee. Nurse Dolores O'Hara took physical particulars before physicians performed a brief examination. Moving to the suit-up room, the three were fitted with their pressure garments by Joe Schmitt. He had been suiting up astronauts since Alan Shepard, and would continue to do so for many more flight to come, finally retiring from NASA in 1982.

The crew left their quarters at 6.27 a.m., the Sun already climbing well above the horizon, the sky blue and serene with only wispy clouds slowly drifting on a 10-knot wind. In 27 minutes they had been driven the 8 miles (13km) to the pad and were being strapped in, plugged in and connected electrically, environmentally and with their respective communications systems by Guenter Wendt – Armstrong first in the left seat, followed by Collins in the right couch and Aldrin in the centre.

Opposite: *More than 40 storeys above the pad, technicians look back at the Apollo 11 Command and Service Modules as the colossal Mobile Service Structure withdraws prior to launch. Note the square "White Room" and No 9 gantry attached to the Launch Umbilical Tower along which the crew will walk to their spacecraft.*

Below: *Neil Armstrong (left) and Buzz Aldrin (right) go through flight procedures in the Lunar Module simulator prior to their mission. Continual refinement of procedures and plans went on right up until the eve of launch day.*

Opposite: *Mike Collins in the Command Module trainer in Building 5 at NASA's Manned Spacecraft Center (now the Johnson Space Center), looking up to the hatch which, when open, allowed access to the interior of the Lunar Module via its own hatch.*

Above: *Neil Armstrong in the simulator looking back towards the rear wall of the Lunar Module. Note the circular access hatch in the roof by which the crew enter or leave the Command Module while docked.*

Left: *Less than three months before their flight, the crew continue rehearsing the procedures that they hope to use on the lunar surface for retrieving small quantities of soil during tests in Building 9 at the Manned Spacecraft Center.*

Right: *To help improve communications with Earth, the astronauts rehearse setting up a large parabolic antennae that they hope to put out on the lunar surface. This was not be used on the first landing but was added to equipment for the second trip to the lunar surface by Apollo 12.*

Opposite: *When Armstrong gets out on to the lunar surface, he will deploy the Modularized Equipment Stowage Assembly (MESA), releasing a TV camera set at an angle so as to show him coming down the ladder, and tools to be used for gathering samples, a procedure here being simulated.*

Below: *Aldrin (left) and Armstrong (right) get to grips with some basic geological principles during training in west Texas.*

Around the world, attention in the news media began to focus on the countdown as the voice of Kennedy Launch Control informed the world of events unfolding in Florida – the site of departure for Jules Verne's imaginary voyage to the Moon – informing listeners that more than a million people were now in Brevard County, specifically there to watch and wait for one of the greatest moments in human history. From the Launch Control Center, the measured, almost monotonic tones of Public Affairs Officer Jack King counted down the seconds, his voice shaking as he reached "zero" and the 3,000-tonne rocket began, slowly at first, to rise from the launch pad.

Above: *Several hundred thousand vehicles, cars and campervans clog the roads across Brevard County waiting and watching for the departure of Armstrong, Collins and Aldrin on their mission to the Moon.*

Left: *Public Affairs Officer Jack King, whose voice was known to millions through his launch commentaries, brought a focused professionalism at the top of a massive pyramid supporting several thousand news correspondents and anchors at the Kennedy Space Center for Apollo 11. In this picture he is the voice of "launch control" for Apollo 12.*

Below: *Former President Lyndon Johnson (in the dark suit), architect of political support for America's national space programme when he was Vice President in 1961, watches the launch of Apollo 11 together with Vice President Spiro Agnew (in the light suit).*

Above: *Chief architect of getting the Apollo spacecraft in fit condition to fly to the Moon, General Sam Phillips (right) stands in the Firing Room at the Launch Control Center as three astronauts are launched on NASA's first attempt to land on the Moon.*

Opposite: *Lift-off! Apollo 11 sets course for the history books from Launch Complex 39A at 9.32 a.m. local time, 16 July 1969 at the Kennedy Space Center.*

Below: *Guidance and Navigation data cards for Apollo 11, which used the Luminary 99 programme. This booklet was used for training purposes on the Lunar Guidance Computer, which was virtually identical to the Apollo Guidance Computer of the Apollo spacecraft.*

Above: *A technician checks the guidance and navigation station with a sextant and telescope located in the configuration in which it was installed in the spacecraft, and the display and keyboard assembly (DISKY) alongside.*

Right: *The Lunar Guidance Computer channel assignment matrix for navigation procedures and programme configurations.*

LGC CHANNEL ASSIGNMENTS

BIT 15	BIT 14	BIT 13	BIT 12	BIT 11	BIT 10	BIT 9	BIT 8	BIT 7	BIT 6	BIT 5	BIT 4	BIT 3	BIT 2	BIT 1	CHANNEL
							+14 RCS B4D	+13 RCS A4U	+16 RCS A2D	+8 RCS B2U	+6 RCS B3D	+5 RCS A3U	+2 RCS A4D	+1 RCS B4U	5
							+16 RCS B1L	+4 RCS A4R	+6 RCS A3R	+12 RCS B2L	+11 RCS A2A	+13 RCS A3F	+3 RCS B4F	+7 RCS B3A	6
RELAY ADRS 4	RELAY ADRS 3	RELAY ADRS 2	RELAY ADRS 1	RELAY ADRS 11	RELAY BIT 11	RELAY BIT 9	RELAY BIT 8	RELAY BIT 7	RELAY BIT 6	RELAY BIT 5	RELAY BIT 4	RELAY BIT 3	RELAY BIT 2	RELAY BIT 1	10
	ENGINE OFF	ENGINE ON			CAUTION RESET			OPERATOR ERROR LAMP	VN FLASH	KEY REL LAMP	TEMP CAUTION LAMP	UPLINK ACTY LAMP	COMPUTER ACTY LAMP	ISS WARNING	11
ISS TURNON DELAY COMPLETE	RR ENABLE AUTO TRK	LR POS 2 COMMAND	+ROLL GIMBAL TRIM	-ROLL GIMBAL TRIM	+PITCH GIMBAL TRIM	-PITCH GIMBAL TRIM	DISPLAY INERTIAL DATA		ENABLE IMU ERROR COUNTER	ZERO IMU CDU	COARSE ALIGN ENABLE		ENABLE RR ERROR COUNTER	ZERO RR CDU	12
ENABLE T6RUPT	RESET TRAP 32	RESET TRAP 31B	RESET TRAP 31A	ENABLE STANDBY	TEST ALARMS	RHC READ	ENABLE RHC CTR	DN LNK WD ORD			RADAR ACTY	RADAR a	RADAR b	RADAR c	13
DRIVE CDUX	DRIVE CDUY	DRIVE CDUZ	DRIVE CDU T	DRIVE CDU S	GYRO ACTY	GYRO MINUS	GYRO a	GYRO b	GYRO ENABLE		THRUST DRIVE	ALT METER	ALT RATE		14
										KEY 5M	KEY 4M	KEY 3M	KEY 2M	KEY 1M	15
										MARK REJECT	MARK X	MARK Y	MARK K		16
TEMP IN LIMITS	ISS TURNON REQUEST	IMU FAIL	ICDU FAIL	IMU CAGE	G & N CONT OF S/C	IMU OPER		RR CDU FAIL	DISPLAY INERTIAL DATA REQ	AUTO THROTTLE	ABORT STAGE (APS)	ENGINE ARMED		ABORT (DPS)	30 *
ATT CONTROL OUT OF DETENT	AUTO STABILIZATION	ATT HOLD	-Z TRANS	+Z TRANS	-Y TRANS	+Y TRANS	-X TRANS	+X TRANS	-AZ (LPD) -RMI	+AZ (LPD) +RMI	-YMI	+YMI	-EL (LPD) -PMI	+EL (LPD) +PMI	31 *
		PROCEED			APPARENT GIMBAL FAIL	GIMBOFF		T 9-12 FAIL	T 10-11 FAIL	T 13-10 FAIL	T 14-16 FAIL	T 5-7 FAIL	T 1-3 FAIL	T 5-8 FAIL	T 2-4 FAIL	32 *
OSC ALARM	COMPUTER WARNING	PIPA FAIL	DNLNK TOO FAST	UPLINK TOO FAST		LR RANG LO SCALE	LR VEL DAT GOOD	LR POS 2	LR POS 1	LR DATA GOOD	RR DATA GOOD	RR RANGE LO SCALE	RR PWR ON AUTO		33 *
15	14	13	12	11	10	9	8	7	6	5	4	3	2	1	

BITS WITHIN DARK LINES ARE PGNCS EXTERNAL INTERFACES
*INVERTED LOGIC

For the crew, ignition of the five F-1 engines at T-8sec brought a low rumble and a little vibration, quickly followed by a significant increase in both sensations as the giant vehicle began its ascent. Local time was 9.32 a.m., one hour earlier in Houston where Mission Control took over when the Saturn V cleared the tower. It was a typical Saturn V launch, all the events up to low Earth orbit going off as for Apollo 8 and with no significant anomalies all the way up, ending at 11min 39sec with the S-IVB and its two spacecraft in an orbit of 116 miles (186km) by 114 miles (183km).

For two orbits the vehicles circled the globe, with Translunar Injection (TLI) – the boost to the Moon – coming at 2hr 44min 16sec, a 5min 47sec burn of the third stage which added 7,118mph (11,452km/h) to its speed and pushed Apollo 11 to escape velocity. Just 27 minutes later Columbia separated from the S-IVB, moved forwards, turned around and docked with Eagle before pulling it free from the inert upper stage.

Some 4hr 40min into the mission, the crew fired Columbia's SPS engine for 3.4 seconds, shifting the predicted lunar close-approach distance from 808 miles (1,300km) to 207 miles (333km). A further correction was made at 26hr 45min, again using the SPS engine for a 2.9-second burst to shift the close-approach point to the desired 72.3 miles (116.3km) from the surface on the far side.

Below left: The page in the LGC Data Cards flip-checklist showing the Digital Auto-Pilot arrangement with the thrusters on the outside of the Lunar Module.

Below right: The list of stars and planets which would be used for manual navigation in the Lunar Module and for conducting alignment measurements to verify that the computer had the correct information.

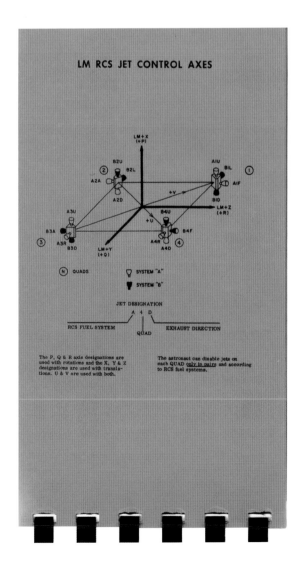

STAR / PLANET LIST

OCTAL STAR CODE	NAME	VIS. MAG.	RIGHT ASCENSION (HR. MIN.)		DECLINATION (DEG. MIN.)	
1	ALPHA ANDROMEDAE (ALPHERATZ)	2.1	0	06	+28	53
2	BETA CETI (DIPHDA)	2.2	0	42	−18	11
3	GAMMA CASSIOPEIAE (NAVI)	2.2	0	54	+60	27
4	ALPHA ERIDANI (ACHERNAR)	0.6	1	36	−57	25
5	ALPHA URSAE MINORIS (POLARIS)	2.1	1	58	+89	06
6	THETA ERIDANI (ACAMAR)	3.4	2	57	−40	26
7	ALPHA CETI (MENKAR)	2.8	3	00	+03	56
10	ALPHA PERSEI (MIRFAK)	1.9	3	22	+49	44
11	ALPHA TAURI (ALDEBARAN)	1.1	4	34	+16	26
12	BETA ORIONIS (RIGEL)	0.3	5	13	−08	15
13	ALPHA AURIGAE (CAPELLA)	0.2	5	13	+45	57
14	ALPHA CARINAE (CANOPUS)	−0.9	6	23	−52	40
15	ALPHA CANIS MAJORIS (SIRIUS)	−1.6	6	44	−16	40
16	ALPHA CANIS MINORIS (PROCYON)	0.5	7	37	+05	19
17	GAMMA VELORUM (REGOR)	1.9	8	08	−47	14
20	IOTA URSAE MAJORIS (DNOCES)	3.1	8	50	+48	30
21	ALPHA HYDRAE (ALPHARD)	2.2	9	26	−08	30
22	ALPHA LEONIS (REGULUS)	1.3	10	06	+12	09
23	BETA LEONIS (DENEBOLA)	2.2	11	47	+14	46
24	GAMMA CORVI (GIENAH)	2.8	12	13	−17	20
25	ALPHA CRUCIS (ACRUX)	1.6	12	24	−62	49
26	ALPHA VIRGINIS (SPICA)	1.2	13	23	−10	58
27	ETA URSAE MAJORIS (ALKAID)	1.9	13	46	+49	30
30	THETA CENTAURI (MENKENT)	2.3	14	04	−36	11
31	ALPHA BOOTIS (ARCTURUS)	0.2	14	14	+19	22
32	ALPHA CORONAE BOREALIS (ALPHECCA)	2.3	15	33	+26	50
33	ALPHA SCORPII (ANTARES)	1.2	16	27	−26	21
34	ALPHA TRIANGULI AUSTR. (ATRIA)	1.9	16	43	−68	56
35	ALPHA OPHIUCHI (RASALHAGUE)	2.1	17	33	+12	35
36	ALPHA LYRAE (VEGA)	0.1	18	36	+38	45
37	SIGMA SAGITTARII (NUNKI)	2.1	18	53	−26	20
40	ALPHA AQUILAE (ALTAIR)	0.9	19	49	+08	46
41	BETA CAPRICORNI (DABIH)	3.2	20	19	−14	54
42	ALPHA PAVONIS (PEACOCK)	2.1	20	23	−56	51
43	ALPHA CYGNI (DENEB)	1.3	20	40	+45	09
44	EPSILON PEGASI (ENIF)	2.5	21	42	+09	42
45	ALPHA PISCIS AUSTRINUS (FOMALHAUT)	1.3	22	56	−29	49
46	SUN					
47	EARTH					
48	MOON					
00	PLANET					

STAR	NO.	STAR	NO.	STAR	NO.
ACAMAR	6	CANOPUS	14	MIRFAK	10
ACHERNAR	4	CAPELLA	13	NAVI	3
ACRUX	25	DABIH	41	NUNKI	37
ALDEBARAN	11	DENEB	43	PEACOCK	42
ALKAID	27	DENEBOLA	23	PROCYON	16
ALPHARD	21	DIPHDA	2	POLARIS	5
ALPHECCA	32	DNOCES	20	RASALHAGUE	35
ALPHERATZ	1	ENIF	44	REGOR	17
ALTAIR	40	FOMALHAUT	45	REGULUS	22
ANTARES	33	GIENAH	24	RIGEL	12
ARCTURUS	31	MENKAR	7	SIRIUS	15
ATRIA	34	MENKENT	30	SPICA	26
				VEGA	36

Well aware of the global interest in this mission, the crew sent an unscheduled TV transmission lasting 16 minutes to the Goldstone, California tracking station, followed by an unscheduled 50-minute transmission at 30hr 28min, then by a scheduled transmission 3hr 31min later lasting 36 minutes. These were "look-around" TV sessions, providing the public with entertaining views inside Columbia. At 55hr 8min the crew began a 96-minute live TV session covering the check of the Lunar Module from opening the hatch to inspecting the interior of Eagle. Excellent views of the crew accomplishing scheduled tasks were interspersed with a view from the LM showing the exterior of the Command/ Service Module and shots of the receding Earth – all in magnificent colour.

The spacecraft passed into the Moon's gravitational influence at 61hr 39min 55sec, some 214,550 miles (345,200km) from Earth and 38,923 miles (62,627km) from its destination – and 14hr 2min before going around the western limb (the apparent edge) of the Moon and out of sight of the Earth. For the crew it was a time for watching and waiting, with several navigation sessions held to determine the horizon altitude for optical marks in the computer. This task was made easier due to the increasing distance and reducing size of the Earth and its limb, upon which the navigations marks were set. But for much of the time the spacecraft was in a Passive Thermal Control "barbecue" roll of 0.3°/sec, about one revolution every 17 minutes, exposing the exterior of the spacecraft to uniform heating from the Sun.

Lasting 6min 2sec, the Lunar Orbit Insertion burn began at 75hr 49min 50sec, and again there were the now-familiar tensions of not knowing for a little while if the SPS had fired correctly or not – too long a burn and it would be putting the docked vehicles into a collision course with the Moon. But the spacecraft appeared from behind the Moon at the expected time after having established the docked spacecraft in a lunar orbit of 195.5 miles (314.5km) by 70 miles (112.6km). The circularization manoeuvre came two orbits later, with a 17-second firing of the SPS engine resulting in a path around the Moon of 79.5 × 62.6 miles (122 × 100.7km).

The first job was to check out Eagle, leaving it fully pressurized after they had verified communication switch positions and decided to leave the probe and drogue stowed rather than place it back in the tunnel as procedures advised, thus saving time. But they were already running behind schedule and were two and a half hours late getting to sleep when they finally signed off at 87hr 30min, resting fitfully until flight surgeon Ken Beers reported all three soundly away.

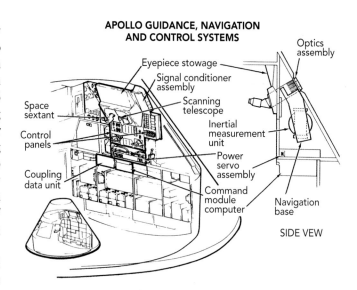

APOLLO GUIDANCE, NAVIGATION AND CONTROL SYSTEMS

SIDE VEW

Above: *The guidance and navigation station in the Apollo Command Module. It was effective during the coast between Earth and Moon for verifying the position of the spacecraft and for conducting navigational checks during lunar orbit, as the Apollo spacecraft could have been required to rescue the Lunar Module had it been stranded in a lower orbit unable to reach the mother ship.*

Below: *The Flight Plan contained data cards, which would be filled in at the appropriate time by an astronaut receiving strings of numbers voiced up to the spacecraft from Mission Control. He would fill in each pad and put those numbers into the computer keyboard. This pad covered computer inputs for the start of powered descent (PDI) down to the surface. In the box at top left, time of ignition (TIG) is displayed in hours, minutes and seconds elapsed time from the moment of launch back on Earth, the time counting down to the braking phase (TGO) and the cross-range value required to adjust the angle of the descent path. Gimbal angle for the flight director attitude indicator (FDAI) is recorded in roll, pitch and yaw (R, P and Y). The other blocks show abort options programmed for less than 10 minutes (< 10 MIN), more than 10 minutes and for an abort back to the orbiting Apollo spacecraft had the PDI burn not taken place, that manoeuvre coming 12 minutes after the scheduled time of ignition.*

FINAL

APOLLO 11
FLIGHT PLAN

AS-506/CSM-107/LM-5

JULY 1, 1969

PREPARED BY
FLIGHT PLANNING BRANCH
FLIGHT CREW SUPPORT DIVISION

MANNED SPACECRAFT CENTER
HOUSTON, TEXAS

Left: *The author's personal copy of the Apollo 11 Flight Plan, a weighty document covering activities to be conducted by the crew for each phase of the mission.*

Below: *The display and keyboard assembly (DSKY – pronounced "diskee") contained all the keys and displays necessary to enter information in verbs and nouns, change programmes in operation and obtain information, advisories and cautions. This DISKY is the configuration used for the Apollo spacecraft, but it is similar to the one used in the Lunar Module.*

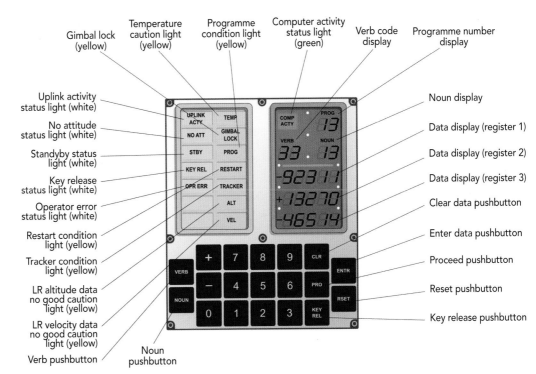

Gimbal lock (yellow)
Temperature caution light (yellow)
Programme condition light (yellow)
Computer activity status light (green)
Verb code display
Programme number display

Uplink activity status light (white)
No attitude status light (white)
Standyby status light (white)
Key release status light (white)
Operator error status light (white)
Restart condition light (yellow)
Tracker condition light (yellow)
LR altitude data no good caution light (yellow)
LR velocity data no good caution light (yellow)
Verb pushbutton
Noun pushbutton

Noun display
Data display (register 1)
Data display (register 2)
Data display (register 3)
Clear data pushbutton
Enter data pushbutton
Proceed pushbutton
Reset pushbutton
Key release pushbutton

Opposite: *Mexico and the south-west United States as seen from Columbia.*

Below: *For two orbits of the Earth, Apollo 11 waited for the "go" to head for the Moon, taking time to snap the occasional picture of the magnificent Earth far below.*

"TRANQUILLITY BASE HERE"

A wake-up call came from Capcom Ron Evans at 93hr 35min. So far, mission events had been comfortably set up for sleep periods closely aligned with the crew's diurnal rhythms; like tourists abroad, they would suffer "travel lag" if moved too far from the biological clock. But this would be a busy day and Armstrong and Aldrin would not get back to sleep for 22 hours. In Houston, it was early morning, 20 July, only a couple of hours past dawn, and for many thousands this would be a long and tiring marathon – the day astronauts walked on the Moon for the first time.

The idea was for Armstrong and Aldrin to transfer to Eagle, close the hatch, separate from Columbia and fire the descent engine on the far side of the Moon, slowing it down and placing it in an elliptical orbit with a low point just 9.5 miles (15.3km) or so above the surface. This much had been done before, on Apollo 10, but unlike the pathfinder mission, this time the LM would now start the powered descent phase, firing up the descent engine and keeping it going continuously, progressively slowing the Lunar Module all the way down to a soft touchdown around 12 minutes later.

As planned, the Descent Orbit Initiation (DOI) burn took place on the far side, at 101hr 36min 14sec, when the engine fired for just under 30 seconds and placed Eagle in an orbit of 65.8 miles (105.9km) by 9.8 miles (15.7km). This was perhaps the most critical manoeuvre conducted at any phase of the mission. If the engine burned just three seconds longer than desired, cutting speed by an additional 8mph (13km/h), Eagle would be on a path that would bring it down to the surface before powered descent could begin.

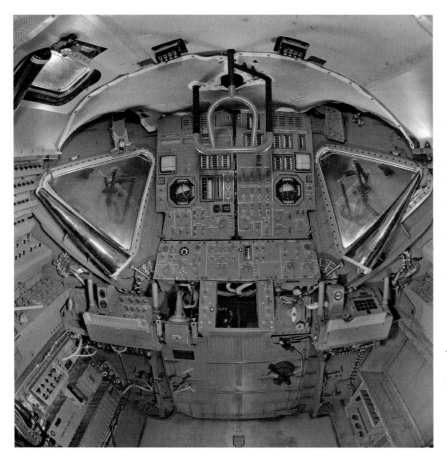

Left: *While Armstrong and Aldrin went down to the lunar surface, Command Module Pilot Mike Collins remained in the Apollo spacecraft, his controls and displays spanning the three couches.*

Opposite above: *Buzz Aldrin in Eagle, where his job was to monitor the instrument displays and do call-outs to Armstrong, who kept his eyes on the surface and controlled the direction of the spacecraft as it neared the surface.*

Opposite below: *A graphic representation of the interior of the Lunar Module looking towards the two forward windows and the central hatch through which Armstrong and Aldrin passed on their way outside to descend the ladder. There were no seats, just tethers and restraints to keep their feet on the floor during weightlessness before landing, after which they had only one-sixth their weight on Earth.*

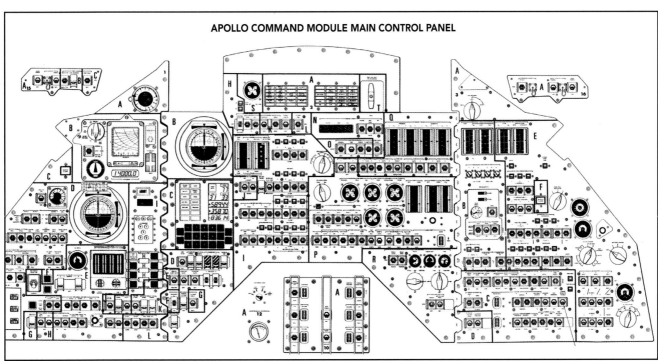

APOLLO COMMAND MODULE MAIN CONTROL PANEL

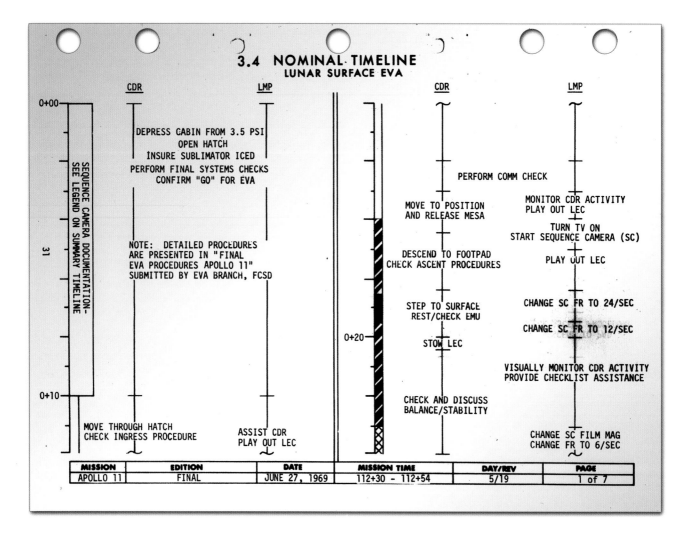

3.4 NOMINAL TIMELINE
LUNAR SURFACE EVA

MISSION	EDITION	DATE	MISSION TIME	DAY/REV	PAGE
APOLLO 11	FINAL	JUNE 27, 1969	112+30 – 112+54	5/19	1 of 7

The DOI burn began at full thrust, then throttled down to 10 per cent for 15 seconds, followed by a throttle-up to 40 per cent for 13 seconds. When they reappeared around the nearside, Armstrong and Aldrin reported that the burn had been on time and correct, and received verification of the orbit from tracking stations on Earth. There was a mere 17 minutes between coming into view around the eastern limb of the Moon and beginning the descent phase, known as Powered Descent Initiation (PDI).

The trajectory followed by Eagle as it descended would follow a shallow glide slope, dropping 9.8 miles (15.7km) in height as it traced a path across the surface 300 miles (483km) in length; only in the very last stages would Eagle arrest its forward motion and begin a vertical descent, landing like a jump jet standing on a pillar of rocket exhaust from the descent engine. Overall, Eagle would slow from 3,790mph (6,100km/h) to zero at touchdown. Before the flight, it was calculated that Eagle stood a 99 per cent chance of landing within a 7.2 × 3 mile (8.3 × 4.8km) ellipse of the selected site, and a 50 per cent chance of getting within an ellipse of 3.9 × 1.4 miles (6.3 × 2.2km).

The entire sequence culminating in a landing was complex and demanding and largely conducted by the on-board Lunar Module Guidance Computer, with the spacecraft orientated so that the crew were facing down towards the surface. Just under three minutes after PDI, at a height of around 44,000ft (13,411m)

Above: *A page from the Lunar Surface Operations Plan which details, across two columns, the first 24 minutes of the time from depressurization of the Lunar Module (technically the start of the surface EVA, or Moonwalk), showing the scheduled time for moving through the hatch and on to the surface. In reality, the crew came out early after forgoing the scheduled four-hour rest after touchdown.*

and having slowed to about 2,725mph (4,384km/h), the spacecraft would roll over so that the crew had their backs to the surface. This would allow the landing radar, which was attached to the bottom of the Descent Stage, to detect the surface and provide input to the navigation system.

Just over eight minutes into the descent phase, 7,500ft (2,286m) above the surface and still travelling at 345mph (555km/h), Eagle would enter High Gate and begin pitching forwards so that the crew could start to observe the surface coming into view from the bottom of the front windows. This process would gradually convert horizontal motion to a vertical position for Low Gate, which would nominally start at a height of 500ft (152m). From here the crew could begin to control the rate of descent, altering the forward and sideways motion so as to avoid any surface obstacles and gradually moving Eagle to a place that appeared smooth and level.

But this was still ahead, as tension began to build in the Manned Spacecraft Center. Behind the "trenches" in the Mission Operations Control Room (MOCR) was a large glass screen separating the flight controllers and mission managers from the dignitaries who began to fill the viewing room behind. All the NASA centre directors were there, all the senior NASA leadership as well as astronauts and some of the key personnel from industry, including Dr Charles Stark Draper, the genius behind the guidance and navigation system that was the single enabling technology which allowed Apollo spacecraft to fly to the Moon and back.

A fleeting seven seconds before the precise time for ignition of the descent engine signalling PDI, four thrusters came on to provide a positive acceleration to settle the propellant in the outlet ducts for the engine's fuel and oxidizer tanks, thereby ensuring a full delivery to the engine and a smooth start, which occurred at precisely 102hr 33min 5.2sec into the mission. For the first 26 seconds the engine operated at 10 per cent thrust before ramping up to 100 per cent thrust for maximum deceleration.

Below: *The author's personal copy of the Lunar Surface Operations Plan, a document containing detailed timelines and explanatory description of various tasks and procedures for working out on the surface of the Moon.*

NATIONAL AERONAUTICS AND SPACE ADMINISTRATION

FINAL

APOLLO 11 LUNAR SURFACE OPERATIONS PLAN

PREPARED BY

LUNAR SURFACE OPERATIONS OFFICE
MISSION OPERATIONS BRANCH
FLIGHT CREW SUPPORT DIVISION

JUNE 27, 1969

MANNED SPACECRAFT CENTER
HOUSTON, TEXAS

At this time Eagle had speeded up as it swooped down to the low point in its orbit and at PDI was, like Snoopy on Apollo 10 before it, about 150 miles (241km) ahead of and far below the Apollo mother ship. In Columbia, Mike Collins was alone and standing by should an abort during Eagle's descent phase become necessary. But as the powered descent phase progressed and Eagle slowed down, Columbia would be at the time of touchdown almost 275 miles (442km) ahead in its orbit around the Moon.

In Houston it was the middle of the afternoon, just after 3.05 p.m.; in London it was just after 9.05 p.m.; radio and television airwaves were awash with wall-to-wall coverage around the globe. Accelerating plans for a global satellite network, the Intelsat organization consisting of representative national telecommunications entities had just in the preceding months completed the launch of satellites in "stationary" orbit (so far out that they keep pace with the rotating Earth). The world got to watch events live as they unfolded – for the first time in most places across the globe, TV offered front row seats, just as the greatest live broadcast in history was taking place.

Below: *A page from the Lunar Surface Operations Plan showing the shadow angles on the surface and the viewing arc of the TV camera on its tripod.*

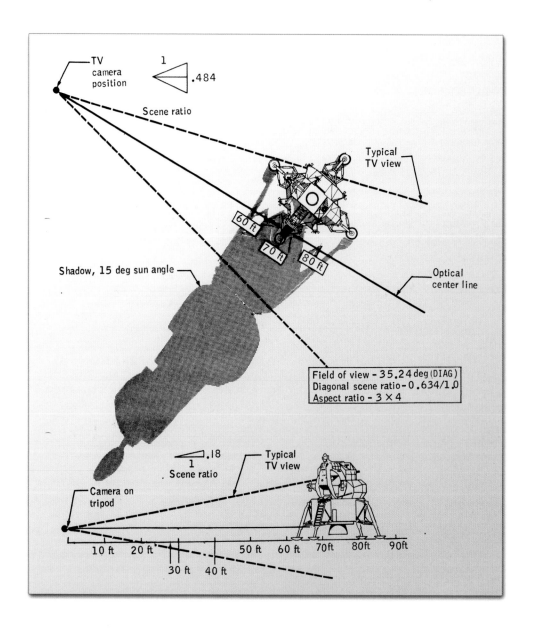

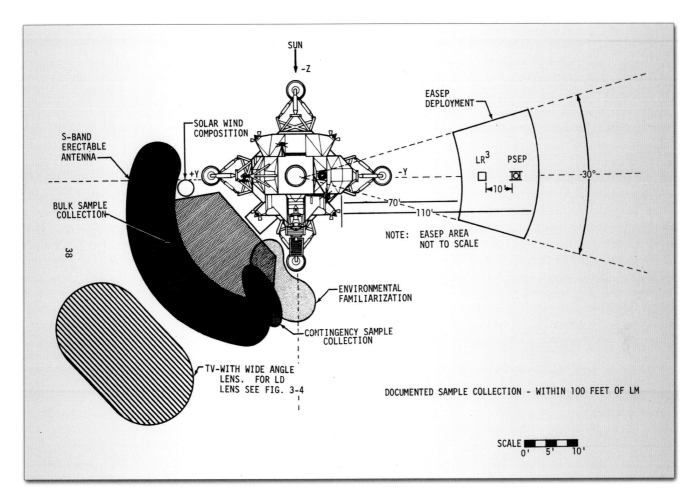

SUN

-Z

EASEP DEPLOYMENT

SOLAR WIND COMPOSITION

S-BAND ERECTABLE ANTENNA

LR³   PSEP

+Y   -Y   -30°

BULK SAMPLE COLLECTION

70'

110'

NOTE: EASEP AREA NOT TO SCALE

38

ENVIRONMENTAL FAMILIARIZATION

CONTINGENCY SAMPLE COLLECTION

TV-WITH WIDE ANGLE LENS. FOR LD LENS SEE FIG. 3-4

DOCUMENTED SAMPLE COLLECTION - WITHIN 100 FEET OF LM

SCALE

0'   5'   10'

For several minutes after Powered Descent Initiation, events proceeded much as planned, tensions high as telemetry flowed back down to Mission Control for instant interpretation – known in the NASA vernacular as "real-time analysis". Armstrong elected to roll to a heads-up attitude at a slower rate than optimized because the autopilot rotation-rate switch was at 5°/sec rather than 25°/sec. The radar did not lock on until an altitude of 37,000ft (11,277m), about 2,000ft (610m) lower than planned and 4min 46sec into the burn. But the data were good and helped balance the computer-generated altitude/velocity projections on the ground with radar data from the spacecraft itself. Roll to the heads-up was fully completed eight seconds later.

Suddenly, at 5min 17sec into the descent phase, a "1202" alarm flashed up in Eagle, also appearing on consoles in Mission Control. The chain of command for any emergency would have Flight Director Gene Kranz get an update from his guidance officer, Steve Bales, as to whether it posed a threat. Hardly anyone in Mission Control knew what a 1202 alarm was, but Bales remembered a similar condition in a simulator, where it was not a critical alarm so long as it did not recur. With the nod from Jack Garman of NASA and Russ Larson of MIT in the back room, Bales passed the word to Kranz, who authorized Capcom Charlie Duke to tell the crew "we are go on that alarm".

Duke's voice was tense as the descent proceeded, the landing radar delivering velocity data at 5min 45sec, and Eagle's speed now down to 1,364mph (2,195km/h). Just 12 seconds later the 1202 alarm flashed again,

Above: The relative location for various activities around the Lunar Module, including the contingency sample obtained early in case the walk had to be aborted, the bulk sample for a wider variety of surface materials, and the documented sample retrieved up to a distance of 100ft (30m) of the LM. Note also the relative locations of the solar wind composition experiment, the laser-ranging retroreflector (LR³) and the passive seismic experiment package (PSEP), placed about 110ft (33.5m) away.

but again the "go" was given to continue powered descent. Up above, Mike Collins was listening in, capable of talking to Mission Control but silent, awaiting perhaps a sudden abort as the tension mounted, the odds gathering against a successful landing. They had practised an in-flight abort on Apollo 10, when the Ascent Stage separated from the Descent Stage, but Neil Armstrong was determined to set Eagle on its perch.

At 6min 26sec the descent engine began to throttle down, matching the diminishing weight of Eagle against the need to progressively reduce speed, but Armstrong had already noted, by visual sight of landmarks familiar to him from training, that Eagle was further down-range than it should be at that point. It was clear to him that the computer was unaware of this: if it had been, it would have held the engine at maximum thrust longer, slowing it faster to compensate. But this detail was not going to halt the descent.

Two minutes went by, and at 8min 27sec Programme 64 went into the Lunar Guidance Computer – High Gate – with Eagle at an altitude of 7,400ft (2,2555m) and sinking

towards the surface at 125ft/sec (38m/sec). The crew were now in the visibility phase and the computer presented information relevant to the Landing Point Designator (LPD), a series of marks on the window, numbered as reticle references to read-outs from the displays showing where the guidance system would put Eagle on the surface without action from the crew.

At 8min 32sec the landing radar was switched to its second position so that it would continue to track the lunar surface below as Eagle pitched over more towards the vertical. Automatic guidance began 26 seconds later, and Gene Kranz went around the room polling his controllers on a "go/no go" for landing, receiving positive responses from the trenches. At precisely 9min 5sec into the descent, Capcom Charlie Duke gave the most historic command in the history of the space programme: "Eagle, Houston. You're go for landing." The Lunar Module was now just 3,000ft (914m) above the Moon.

Seconds later, another alarm popped up – a 1201 – but this was not fatal to the mission and less of a problem

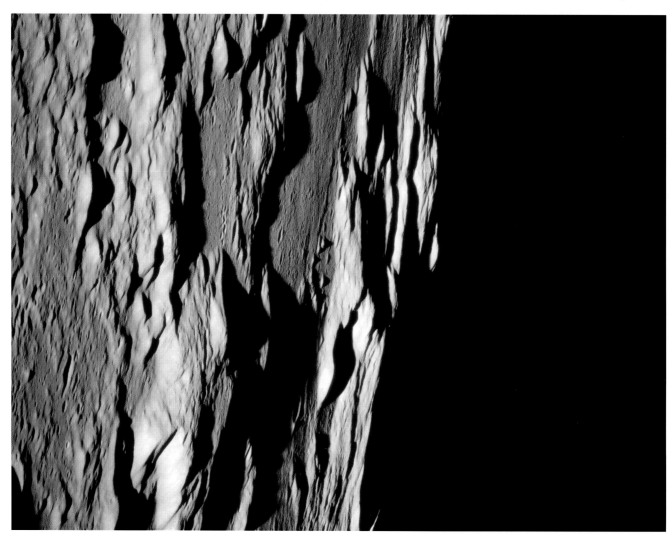

than the 1202 potentially could be. The 1201 was a different segment of the same executive overflow that occurred earlier and Duke rapidly urged them to keep going. Under Programme 64 the crew would normally have been focused intently on managing the final landing phase, with Armstrong in control of Eagle and Aldrin reading out the displays and advising him of relevant information. But now their attention was split between restoring computer data and visually looking at the surface below for features they could recognize.

Then another 1202 flashed up at 9min 38sec, and yet again 15 seconds later. Still they got a "go" to continue, judgement based on the fact that at this point Armstrong was now able to make manual inputs to physically shape the path of the trajectory as Eagle descended ever closer to the surface. But distractions caused by alarms, the fact that Eagle was further down-range than had been realized and the unfamiliar nature of what now appeared to be a surface not flat but strewn with boulders caused Armstrong to take time and precious propellant to manoeuvre the Lunar Module away from obstacles.

A product of endless calculations and simulations, the descent to the surface from Powered Descent Initiation to engine shutdown was expected to take 11min 58sec – give or take a few seconds for manoeuvring close to the ground. At an elapsed time of 11min 39sec the low-level propellant quantity light came

Opposite: *Without an atmosphere to disperse light, an important part of mission planning was providing Armstrong and Aldrin with the correct visual conditions, ensuring that the angle of the Sun was not too low to make it hard to pick out surface obstacles in long shadows, as here.*

Below: *Correct lighting angles allowed a balance between deep black shadows and a total light-rich washout – this view being an ideal Sun angle for discriminating between hidden and exposed threats.*

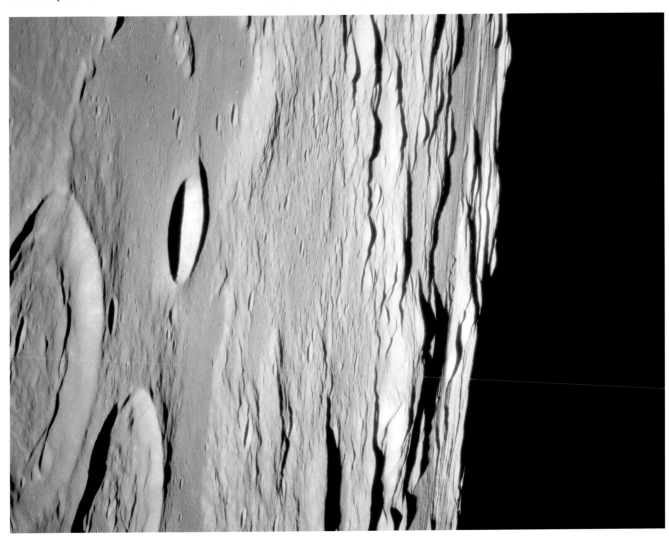

on, and 18 seconds later, with Eagle still 60ft (18m) above the surface and searching for a safe spot, Charlie Duke threw out a cautionary "60 seconds" to the crew, indicating that they had a minute left before they would have to either put the craft down or abort.

The seconds continued to tick by as Armstrong moved Eagle forwards and then to the right, his right hand on the attitude control stick, searching constantly for a space between the rocks and the shallow craters. "30 seconds," came the call from Charlie Duke – 12min 26sec and still 30ft (9m) off the ground. So close, so very close, and the calm and collected Armstrong was still searching as the descent engine began to pick up dust off the surface. In Mission Control the telemetry showed his heartbeat at 150 per minute.

Below: *A pass across the Apollo 11 landing site as viewed from Columbia orbiting above, the flat and apparently smooth surface belying the reality – as Armstrong found when he neared the surface and searched for a safe spot to land.*

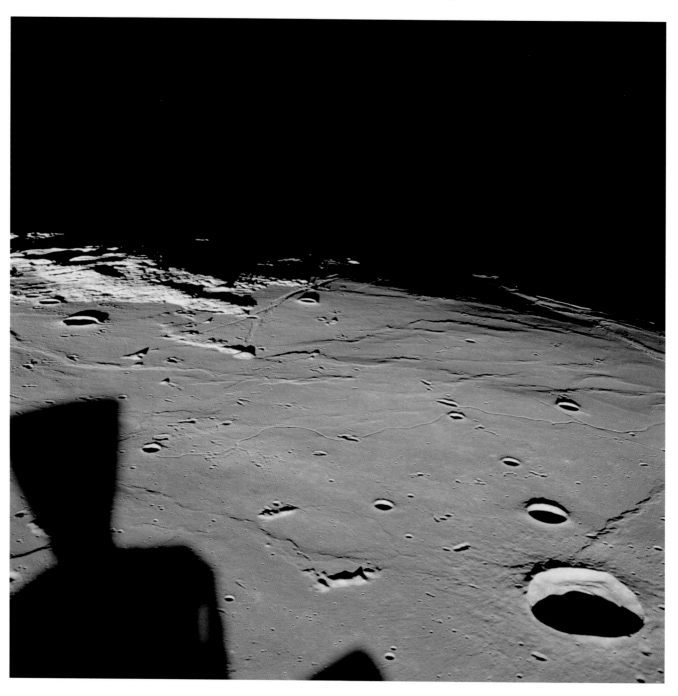

Throughout Mission Control there was a belief that Eagle was about to run out of propellant, and without that the Lunar Module would fall to the surface, albeit at only one-sixth the rate it would on Earth due to the reduced gravity. But it would be a sufficient shock, even from this height, to potentially fracture a critical life-support system or, at worst, damage the vehicle to the extent that the Ascent Stage would be unable to lift off to carry the crew back to Columbia.

A probe 6ft (1.7m) long was attached to three of the four landing legs (but not the leg supporting the ladder down which the crew would climb to reach the surface); its contact sensor would illuminate a light on the display panel

Above: *Separated from Columbia, Eagle prepares to descend towards the surface of the Moon, 20 July 1969. This picture was taken from Columbia.*

when it touched the surface. That light came on 12min 35sec after the descent engine had begun firing, provoking an exultant shout of "Contact light!" from Buzz Aldrin. Eagle slowly settled to the lunar surface. Two men had just landed on the Moon. In Houston it was shortly before 3.18 p.m. – in London it was 9.18 p.m. and the mission elapsed time clock on the wall of Mission Control read 102hr 45min 40sec.

Precisely 19 seconds later came the first sentences from the surface of another world when Neil Armstrong acknowledged their arrival: "Houston, Tranquillity Base here," and after a slight pause, five seconds later: "The Eagle has landed."

Released briefly from their tensions, flight controllers erupted with a spontaneous cheer as Capcom Charlie Duke, who had talked the astronauts all the way down to the surface, fought for an appropriate response: "Roger, Tranquillity. We copy you on the ground. You got a bunch of guys about to turn blue. We're breathing again. Thanks a lot."

To the flight controllers it was an unbelievable moment. Flight Director Gene Kranz momentarily froze, while beyond the glass screen people were clapping and cheering. But there was no respite. The first job was to verify that everything aboard Eagle was working as it should and verify whether it could remain on the surface. This was referred to as T1 and was one of two contingency lift-off times in the event that the landing had damaged the vehicle. If it had been damaged there would be immediate preparations for a lift-off; T2 came nine minutes after touchdown. Neither was needed. Eagle was safe in its nest.

Alone in his spacecraft, Mike Collins went around the west limb of the Moon to the far side and lost contact with Earth some 42 minutes after Eagle touched down. Each time Columbia came round to the nearside there was an opportunity for Eagle to leave the surface and rendezvous with the mother ship. But those early departures too would not be needed – the lunar stay could last its planned duration.

Opposite: Shadowed in a low Sun angle, this photograph taken from Columbia shows Eagle sitting on the surface ready for the first Moonwalk in history.

THE SCRIPT FOR A EULOGY

At the suggestion of astronaut Frank Borman, speechwriter William Safire wrote a message for President Nixon to read out to the nation should the crew become stranded on the Moon, and sent it to White House Chief of Staff H.R. Haldeman. It begins: "Fate has ordained that the men who went to the Moon to explore in peace will stay on the Moon to rest in peace," declaring: "In ancient days, men looked at stars and saw their heroes in the constellations. In modern times we do much the same, but our heroes are epic men of flesh and blood."

The short speech went on to affirm: "Others will follow, and surely find their way home. Man's search will not be denied. But these men were the first, and they will remain the foremost in our hearts."

It ended with an echo of Rupert Brooke's World War I poem "The Soldier" – "there's some corner of a foreign field/That is forever England". Safire's speech contorted this when he concluded his text with: "There is some corner of another world that is forever mankind," a reference some felt should have been left out, and one which may have caused rumblings of sadness that Brooke's words, born from the negativity of the 20th century, should be used in this way – and singularly inappropriate given that, as Safire asserted, "Others will follow...".

CHAPTER 10

ONE SMALL STEP

Under the finally approved flight plan, Armstrong and Aldrin were to carry out some checks on Eagle, photograph the lunar surface through the windows and start a meal about two hours after landing. After 40 minutes they were to rest for four hours before getting ready for working outside on the surface. This was to have Armstrong leave Eagle about 10 hours after touchdown, followed by Aldrin around 20 minutes later, then they were both to have set up a US flag and deployed some experiments on the surface – around breakfast time in the United States. Some 600 million people around the world were waiting to watch it live.

It didn't go that way. Before the flight began, the crew had worked up an alternative plan to go out early, a hedge against any problem arising in Eagle which would require them to lift-off prematurely for a rendezvous with Columbia. That was exactly the way it went.

Preparations for the Moonwalk took longer than expected. Before that began, about 2hr 20min after touchdown, Aldrin asked people all over the world to stop what they were doing and participate: "I'd like to take this opportunity to ask every person listening in, whoever and wherever they may be, to pause for a moment and contemplate the events of the past few hours, and to give thanks in his or her own way." He then proceeded to take Holy Communion, a ceremony he had received permission from the Pope to conduct.

A WALK IN THE SUN

Getting suited up took longer than expected, but 6hr 23min after touchdown, Armstrong reported, "The hatch is coming open." It was a small, square hatch, only 21in (8cm) on each side, with a hinge on the right facing forwards from the inside. Located at floor level, it called for the suited astronaut to get down on all fours and back out through the hatch onto a small platform, known as the "porch", before descending backwards down the nine rungs of the ladder.

A clear 12 minutes later, Armstrong reported that he was on the porch. There he pulled a lanyard that deployed a box of equipment from a hinge down on the right-hand forward side of the Descent Stage. This automatically triggered a TV camera that began transmitting when Aldrin threw a switch in the cabin, and a picture appeared from the surface of the Moon. Just 15 minutes after

Above: *Buzz Aldrin begins to emerge from Eagle, as photographed by Neil Armstrong, already on the surface.*

Above: *Weighing only one-sixth his Earth weight, Aldrin carefully feels for the top rung on the ladder as he begins his descent to the surface.*

Right: *The lower rung of the ladder was a big step above the surface due to the lack of compression in the landing legs, indicating a gentle touchdown.*

operating the hatch, Capcom confirmed to Armstrong: "Neil, we can see you coming down the ladder now."

Before stepping off the footpad, Armstrong checked getting back up to the first rung – some way off the ground because the compressible strut had collapsed only a very small amount. Just 17 minutes after opening the hatch, he reported: "I'm at the foot of the ladder. The LM footpads are only depressed in the surface about one or two inches, although the surface appears to be very, very fine grained, as you get close to it. It's almost like a powder. Down here, it's very fine. I'm going to step off the LM now."

Nobody quite knew what Armstrong was going to say. But when he uttered the now historic words a minute later, it was a simple and clear statement, followed almost immediately by observations on the surface texture.

"That's one small step for [a] man, one giant leap for mankind. And the – the surface is fine and powdery – I can pick it up loosely with my toe. It does adhere in fine layers like powered charcoal to the sole and sides of my boots. I only go in a small fraction of an inch, maybe an eighth of an inch, but I can see the footprints of my boots and the treads in the fine, sandy particles."

Below: *The poor quality of the picture seen on TV screens around the world served only to reinforce the surreal nature of the images from this iconic live broadcast.*

Those first historic words from the surface of another world began at a mission elapsed time of 109hr 24min 45sec. In Houston it was 9.56 p.m. on Sunday, 20 July 1969, and in the United Kingdom it was six hours later – just before 4.00 a.m.; there and in Europe it was already Monday. A few minutes later, Armstrong mused over the view that lay before him: "It has a stark beauty all its own. It's like much of the high desert of the United States. It's different but it's very pretty out here."

The first job was to take a contingency sample, just in case the mission had to be aborted, quickly secured in one of Armstrong's pockets. Then came Aldrin, who was already on the porch: "Now I want to back up and partially close the hatch. Making sure not to lock it on my way out." Aldrin was on the surface 19 minutes after his commander and immediately set about orientating himself to the reduced gravity.

There were many sundry tasks before the main job of laying out a couple of science instruments: placing on the surface a small microdot containing messages from numerous world leaders, relocating the TV camera to a tripod 80ft (25m) away so that viewers could see more of the action, giving viewers a conducted tour of the surface and setting up a solar-wind experiment provided by Switzerland to measure the charged particles coming from the Sun. These were followed by the erection of the US flag – clearly defined as not indicating a national claim on the Moon or any part of its surface but merely as a recognition of national effort.

Above: *Aldrin's boot print on the dusty surface of the Moon. A powdery material known as regolith, with the consistency of wet beach sand and smelling of burnt gunpowder, it sticks like glue to any surface, including space suits.*

Following pages: *The only good photograph of Neil Armstrong on the entire Moonwalk was taken during removal of equipment from Eagle. It was Armstrong's job to document events with a camera, and nobody really thought through the implication of that – no one had specifically been tasked with photographing Armstrong!*

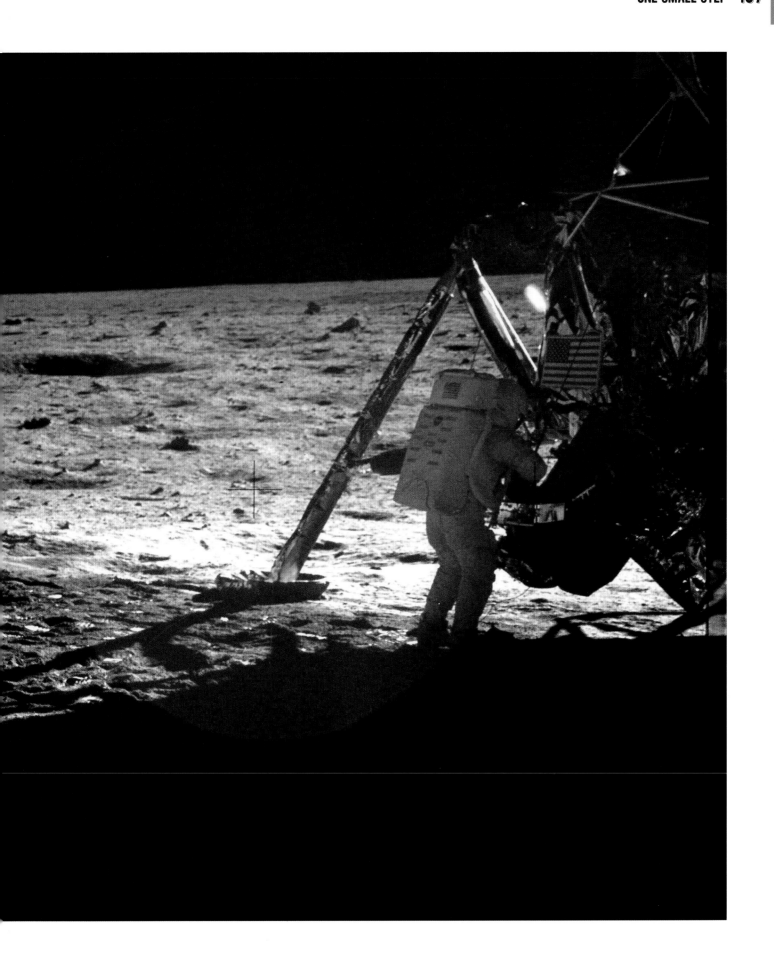

THE MOON SUIT

Throughout the development of rockets and spacecraft, an unexpected challenge was the space suit, one capable of protecting its wearer from the extreme heat and cold of airless space, insulating the body from micrometeorite impacts, providing a life-support system with oxygen and coolant, and ensuring a means of maintaining contact with fellow astronauts and Mission Control.

To prevent ballooning and stiffness, the oxygen pressure was kept as low safely possible. The spacecraft had a pressure of 5lb/sq in (34.75kPa) while the suit was pressurized to a safe 3.9lb/sq in (26.89kPa). The suit itself was required to withstand temperatures of +/- 250°F (+121°C to -156°C).

From the skin out, the astronaut wore a knitted nylon-spandex garment with a network of plastic tubing through which cooling water was circulated from the life-support pack. The suit itself consisted of a Nomex comfort layer, a neoprene-coated nylon pressure bladder and a nylon restraint layer. The outer layers consisted of an inner Nomex lining and two layers of Teflon-coated Beta cloth with an integrated thermal/meteoroid cover, which itself consisted of two layers of neoprene-coated nylon, seven layers of Beta/Kapton spacer laminate and an outer layer of Teflon-coated Beta fabric.

Most difficult of all to engineer were the gloves. They were built up under an outer shell of Chromel-R fabric and thermal insulation with fingertips made of silicone rubber to provide greater touch sensitivity. The helmet consisted of a polycarbonate shell and two visors with optical coatings.

The backpack, or Personal Life Support System (PLSS), was required to support an astronaut for four hours on the Moon. Later versions would support Moonwalks lasting up to eight hours. The PLSS weighed 41lb (19kg) on Earth, a mere 6.8lb (3.1kg) in the one-sixth gravity of the Moon. It was surmounted by an Oxygen Purge System (OPS), an emergency backup unit which could keep an astronaut alive for 30 minutes in the event that his primary backpack failed.

In a so-called "buddy system" configuration, cooling water connected to a fellow astronaut's PLSS could extend this to a maximum 90 minutes via a connecting hose. A Remote Control Unit (RCU) was attached to the astronaut's chest for adjusting settings and control functions. Overall, the suit, the PLSS, the OPS and the RCU were known as the Extravehicular Mobility Unit (EMU).

The Apollo A7L suit had first been tested during the Earth-orbiting Apollo 9 mission, when Rusty Schweickart had spent 1hr 17min evaluating its performance. Its next workout was when Neil Armstrong and Buzz Aldrin dressed up for the Moonwalk.

Oxygen Purge System

Life Support System

Opposite: *The A7L Extravehicular Mobility Unit (EMU) had evolved through several design changes, modifications based upon previous experience and the gradually improving capabilities of life-support equipment. The suit would itself evolve, as shown here with considerable improvements to the visors.*

Left: *The interior of the Personal Life Support System designed to support an astronaut on the Moon for several hours of exploration.*

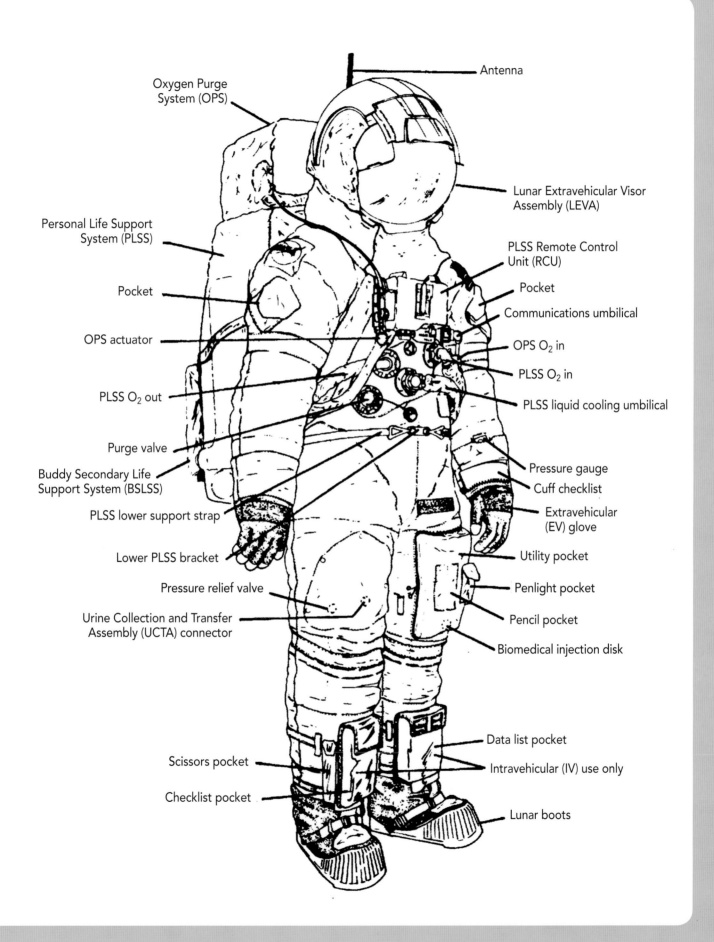

Antenna

Oxygen Purge
System (OPS)

Lunar Extravehicular Visor
Assembly (LEVA)

Personal Life Support
System (PLSS)

PLSS Remote Control
Unit (RCU)

Pocket

Pocket

OPS actuator

Communications umbilical

OPS O₂ in

PLSS O₂ in

PLSS O₂ out

PLSS liquid cooling umbilical

Purge valve

Pressure gauge

Buddy Secondary Life
Support System (BSLSS)

Cuff checklist

PLSS lower support strap

Extravehicular
(EV) glove

Lower PLSS bracket

Utility pocket

Pressure relief valve

Penlight pocket

Urine Collection and Transfer
Assembly (UCTA) connector

Pencil pocket

Biomedical injection disk

Data list pocket

Scissors pocket

Intravehicular (IV) use only

Checklist pocket

Lunar boots

And then, 51 minutes after Armstrong had stepped on to the surface, it was time for President Richard M. Nixon to speak to Armstrong and Aldrin: "Neil and Buzz, I am talking to you from the White House and this certainly has to be the most historic telephone call ever made…. Because of what you have done, the heavens have become a part of Man's world. And as you talk to us from the Sea of Tranquillity it inspires us to double our efforts to bring peace and tranquillity to Earth. For one priceless moment, in the whole history of Man, all the people on this Earth are truly one."

As they went about their tasks, the two Moonwalkers made frequent comments about the nature of the surface, the rocks and craters large and small, and the minimal impact the landing had imposed on the surface. By this time Aldrin was behind Eagle retrieving the two packages of science experiments that formed part of what NASA called the Early Apollo Scientific Experiments Package, or ESAP, denoted as "early" because each subsequent landing would carry a much larger second-generation array of instruments powered by a nuclear power source, equipment that would obtain data and send it back to stations on Earth for several years.

Below: *Three of Eagle's landing legs carried contact sensor probes that extended directly downwards. They were supposed to be crushed on landing to absorb the impact, but Armstrong landed so delicately that the legs didn't crumple and the step down from Eagle was higher than intended. This is why the first step was actually more of a "leap".*

Above: *The underside of Eagle's Descent Stage, showing little erosion from the engine exhaust and no damage to the nozzle, the bottom edge of which was 12in (30cm) above the surface.*

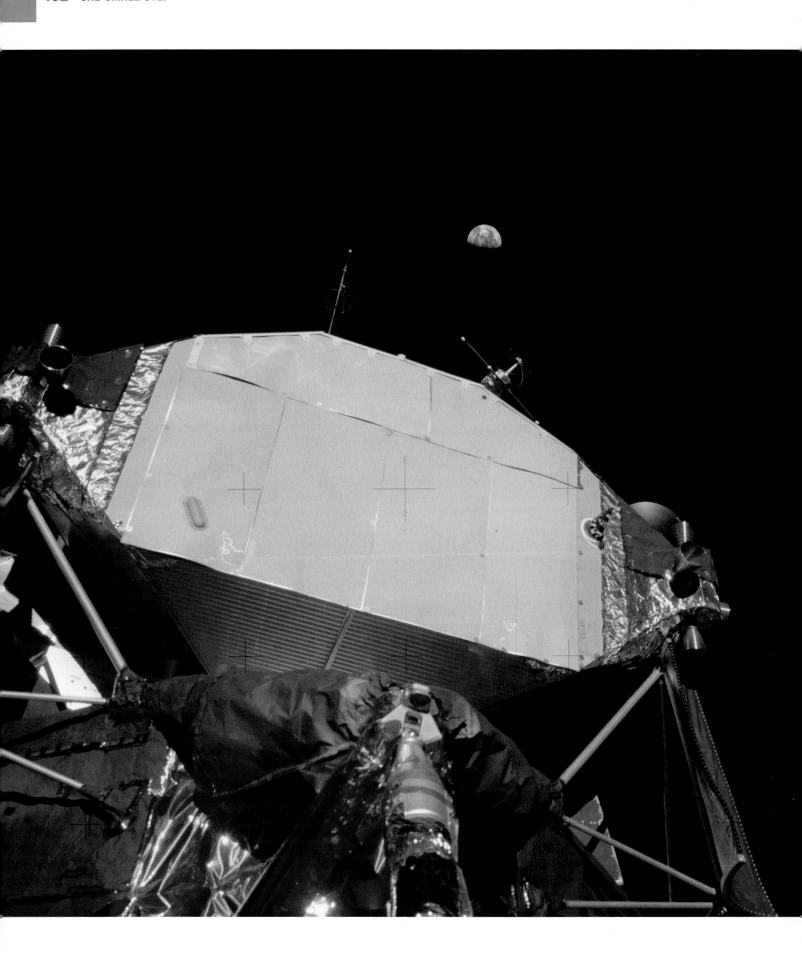

Opposite: *The back of Eagle with the two aft thruster quads clearly visible and their plume deflectors to prevent hot gases burning the thermal insulation. The Earth sits between two antennae: the small UF antenna (top right) is used to communicate with Earth, and the pole-like Moonwalk antenna (top left) is for receiving voice and data from the suits for onward transmission to Earth.*

Above: *The plaque to be left on the Moon was one of the last additions to the Lunar Module, since it was not certain until after Apollo 10 that the next flight would be the actual landing attempt.*

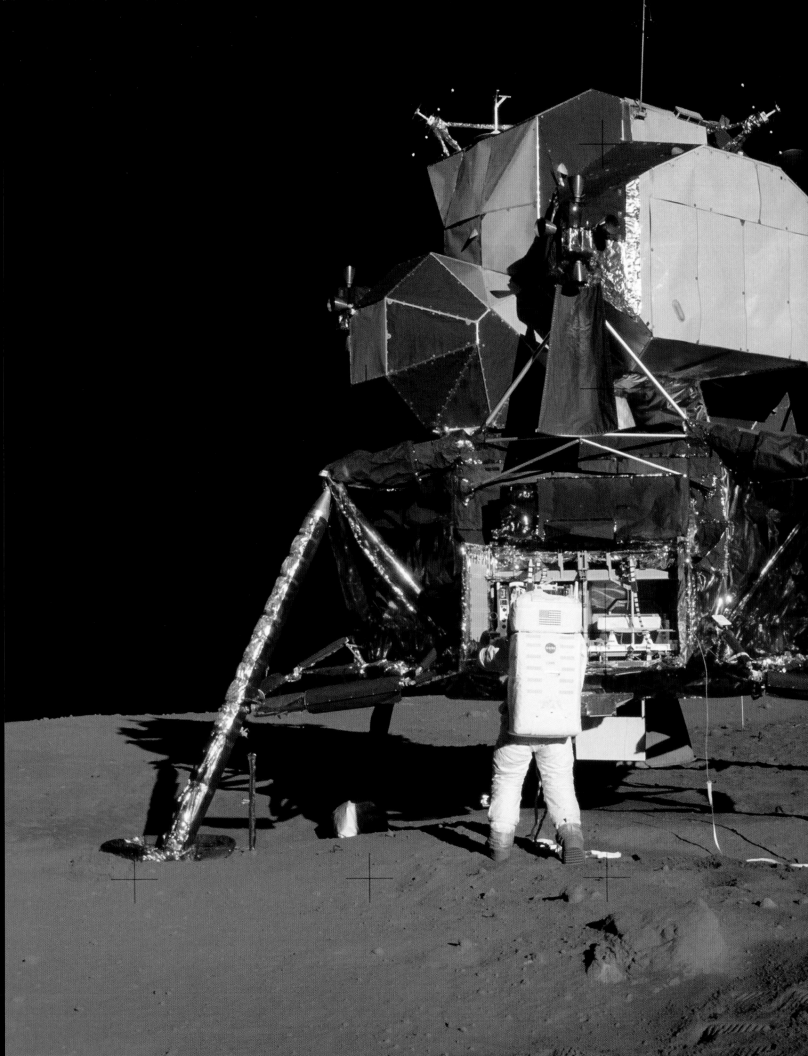

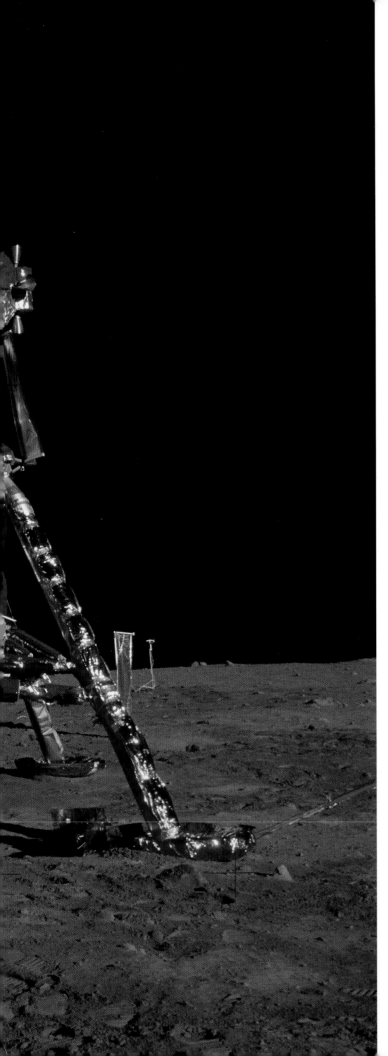

Left: *Buzz Aldrin removes equipment from the left rear stowage compartment on Eagle's Descent Stage – instruments that will be deployed on the surface.*

The only two science instruments left on the surface were a passive seismometer powered by solar cells, to detect Moonquakes, and a laser reflector which is still used today. This, together with two more left on subsequent missions, allows triangulation to record reflections of lasers beamed from Earth that show that the Moon is drifting away at the rate of 1.5in (3.8cm) per year while on Earth the separate North American and Eurasian plates are moving apart at 2.5in (1cm) each year.

All too soon it was time to wrap up activity and head back into Eagle. Aldrin rolled up the solar-wind experiment, essentially an aluminium foil sheet, 4.6ft (1.4m) by 12in (30cm) hung from a pole planted in the surface for the duration of the Moonwalk. Aldrin left the surface after spending 1hr 50min roaming Tranquillity Base and was followed by Armstrong who had been there 41 minutes longer. Some 2hr 32min after opening the hatch for the Moonwalk, Aldrin reported that it was closed and locked, mission elapsed time of 111hr 39min. In Houston it was after midnight and in London it was just after 6.00 a.m. on 21 July.

Left: *Equipment left on the Moon included the passive seismometer with solar panels (foreground), the laser-ranging retro-reflector beyond, the flag, and the TV camera on a tripod on the far side of Eagle.*

Still in their space suits, the crew depressurized Eagle for a second time at 114hr 7min, to throw out their life-support backpacks (excess weight that could be left on the Moon), as well as some redundant items. Their impact was recorded in data from the passive seismometer. Then followed a lengthy discussion about mobility on the surface, the texture of lunar soil and the general terrain, plus comments about deployment of the EASAP. Mission Control finally said goodnight to the crew at around 115hr – almost 22 hours after their last rest period in lunar orbit when they had still been docked to Columbia.

Armstrong chose to rig himself a hammock with a waist tether and slept on the engine cover, while Aldrin curled up on the floor. They were awoken after little more than six hours at 121hr 40min. They had been on the surface for almost 18 hours and it was time to begin setting up the systems for departure. Another critical moment at which, if the engine failed to fire or sputtered out on the way up, there was nothing anyone could do to save the crew, this was to be the second launch on this mission, and the first time a manned spacecraft had lifted off from the surface of another world.

Opposite: *Aldrin poses to provide a good view of the front of the Extravehicular Mobility Unit (EMU), with hoses for oxygen in (blue connectors), oxygen out (red), the Remote Control Unit (RCU) on his chest, and the polycarbonate helmet with visor.*

Below: *Back in the Lunar Module, a view through the right window showing the flag and the TV camera, with footprints which, if undisturbed, will remain there for millions of years.*

The loneliness Collins was experiencing on each pass around the far side of the Moon was evoked for Earth-based listeners by the Voice of Mission Control. "Not since Adam has any human known such solitude as Mike Collins is experiencing during this 47 minutes of each lunar revolution when he's behind the Moon with no one to talk to except his tape recorder aboard Columbia."

SAILING HOME

The ascent engine was designed to carry the crew back into orbit by means of a burn lasting 7min 20sec. With a thrust of 3,500lb (15.57kN), it would propel the two-man crew to a speed of 4,138mph (6,658km/h) and to an orbit of 52 × 10.3 miles (84 × 16km). When the Ascent Stage lifted off from the Descent Stage it weighed 10,776lb (4,888kg), or approximately 1,800lb (816kg) under one-sixth lunar gravity. Thus the ascent engine could lift it back into space with a mass only one-third its Earth weight, reduced to 5,928lb (2,689kg) after it had burned off its propellant.

At lift-off, Columbia would be 95 miles (152km) up ahead, but when it arrived in orbit the Ascent Stage would be 304 miles (490km) behind, although, being in a lower orbit, what remained of Eagle would begin to reduce that. Over the next six hours a complex sequence of rendezvous manoeuvres, techniques tried during the two-man Gemini programme and rehearsed during Apollos 9 and 10, brought the two vehicles together.

Around the world, people watched on TVs or listened to their radios or caught flashed news headlines on buildings. After the euphoria of the past 24 hours, tension mounted again. Finally, at an elapsed time of 124hr 22min 0.8sec, the ascent engine lifted the Moonwalkers away from the surface exactly as planned, the only comment from Aldrin being a nonchalant "beautiful".

Eagle had been on the surface of the Moon for 21hr 36min 20sec, during which the first Moonwalk had lasted a total 2hr 21min 40sec. The two astronauts had collected 47.5lb (21.5kg) of rocks, soil, pebbles and other lunar material, much of which would be shared among scientists in many nations on Earth.

After the coordinated sequence of rendezvous manoeuvres, Eagle's Ascent Stage docked with Columbia at 128hr 03min, almost 28 hours after undocking. In Houston it was late afternoon; in London it was late at night, after 10.00 p.m.. Just over two hours later, after Armstrong and Aldrin had rejoined Collins and unnecessary materials had been put back in Eagle, the Ascent Stage was jettisoned, its work done.

And then it was back to business, with Mission Control reading the astronauts reams of numbers and data to feed into the Apollo Guidance Computer ready for the all-important Trans-Earth Injection (TEI) burn of Columbia's main engine. As with deceleration into lunar orbit, that burn would come on the far side of the Moon and until Columbia came around the eastern limb it would not be possible to know if the vital firing had occurred.

Loss-of-signal (LOS) occurred at 134hr 57min, some 26 minutes before Columbia's main engine was scheduled to fire for 2min 30sec, speeding up the spacecraft by 2,190mph (3,523km/h). If that burn went as planned, Columbia would appear from the far side 37 minutes after LOS; if not, it would be a further 10 minutes before the spacecraft appeared – still in lunar orbit.

In Houston it was just after midnight as the clock slipped into a new day – 22 July. In London it was just after 6.00 a.m. Right on time, at 135hr 34min 5sec, Mission Control began to see data flowing back down through

Opposite: *A satisfied commander, Neil Armstrong – mission accomplished!*

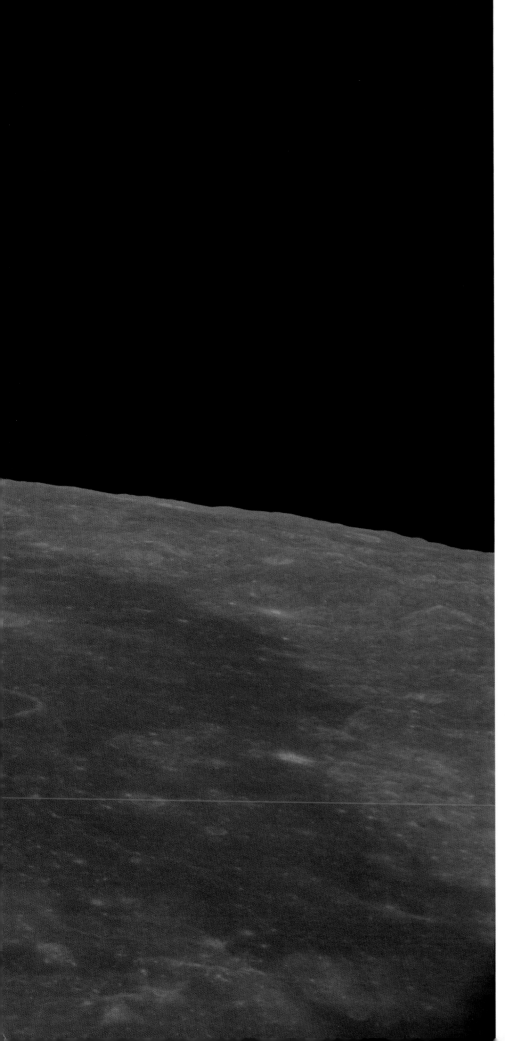

the tracking stations on Earth. On a call from Capcom Charlie Duke, Mike Collins responded with "Time to open up the LRL doors, Charlie!", referring to the Lunar Receiving Laboratory that was the depository at the Manned Spacecraft Center where some of the most precious rocks collected from anywhere would reside before loan distribution to laboratories around the world.

The course set by the Trans-Earth Injection (TEI) burn had been almost perfect but a tweak was performed at 150hr 30min by the small thruster quads on the Service Module, changing speed by a mere 3.2mph (5.1km/h) and setting up the re-entry corridor for a perfect return to a Pacific Ocean splashdown. The first lunar explorers were coming home, and in the less than 60 hours before splashdown they would conduct navigation sightings, put the spacecraft in a passive thermal control roll to distribute the heat from the Sun and catch up on sleep.

By mid-evening in Houston, deep night in London, a vase of long-stemmed red roses had been delivered to Mission Control with a note saying: "To one and all concerned. Job superbly done. From a Moonstruck Canadian." It was the first of a long tradition of flower gifts that would accompany every Moon mission.

There were TV transmissions too. At 20 hours after TEI came an 18-minute broadcast, showing a world still in awe what it was like inside the spacecraft, to eat and drink and what the Moon and the Earth looked like through the windows. Another TV transmission was broadcast beginning at 177hr 32min elapsed time,

Left: *The Lunar Module Ascent Stage rejoins Columbia with Mike Collins inside, who had remained in orbit.*

during which each member of the crew expressed their own feelings about the flight and about the challenge laid down less than 3,000 days before.

They spoke about their passionate connection to the work and the dedication that made it possible, and about the deeper meaning of what they had just done, expressed by Buzz Aldrin in his closing comment: "Personally, on reflecting [on] the events of the past several days, a verse from Psalms comes to mind to me: 'When I consider the heavens, the work of Thy fingers, the Moon and the stars which Thou has ordained, what is man that Thou are mindful of him.'"

It fell to Neil Armstrong to close the last TV transmission from Apollo 11 by reminding all the hundreds of millions watching on Earth: "The responsibility for this flight lies first with history and with the giants of science who have preceded this effort. Next with the American people who have through their will, indicated their desire."

Armstrong went on to acknowledge the political leadership across four Presidential administrations and the Congressional support "for implementing that will and to the agency and industry teams that built our spacecraft, the Saturn, the Columbia, the Eagle, and the little EMU – the space suit and backpack that was our small spacecraft out on the lunar surface…. To those people tonight we give a special thank you and, to all the other people that are listening and watching tonight, God bless you. Goodnight from Apollo 11." Columbia was still 105,000 miles (168,945km) from Earth with more than 17 hours to go before splashdown.

The crew were awakened by Mission Control with a little less than six hours to go before re-entry. Deteriorating weather shifted the planned landing zone 247 miles (397km) down-range, but conditions there were near perfect, as befitted this historic mission: visibility was 14 miles (22.5km), wave height a modest 3ft (1m) and wind at 16 knots. All the preparatory events went like clockwork: power was switched from the Service Module supplies and expendables to the Command Module's internal resources before the latter and its three-man crew, with precious rock samples, separated and turned around for the dramatic fireball that accompanied re-entry.

Visual contact with Columbia was obtained 12 minutes before splashdown and landing occurred 14 minutes after re-entry, at 195hr 18min 35sec and a position 13° 19' N by 169.9° 9' W. In Houston it was 11.50 a.m. and in London it was early evening – by coincidence, prime TV time, on Thursday, 24 July. The Command Module flipped over to Stable 2, apex-down in the water, but flotation bags righted the module within seven minutes.

Left: *The USS* Hornet *recovers the Command Module from the Pacific Ocean at the end of the historic first mission to the Moon.*

Deployed from a recovery helicopter, John McLachlan, Terry Muehlenbach and Mitchell Bucklew were the first men to reach the Command Module to fit a stabilizing flotation collar before tossing biological isolation garments (BIGs) through the open hatch for the crew to don. The recovery ship USS *Hornet* had the crew on board 63 minutes after splashdown, but it was straight into a Mobile Quarantine Facility (MQF), where they would remain until airlifted to Houston.

The MQF was a biologically insulated Airstream trailer specially converted for the job of isolating any germs or bacterial contamination from the rest of the world's 3.5 billion people. The crew would be released from it on 10 August, when physicians were sure that no extraterrestrial bugs had been let loose on the planet. Thereafter, for Armstrong, Collins and Aldrin, life would change forever, with a seemingly endless parade of formal events, across the United States and around the world.

LEGACY OF APOLLO

After its first six years, NASA's rapidly escalating budget came to a halt and even began to fall in 1965, four years before Apollo 11. Sufficient rockets and spacecraft had been manufactured to support flights through to Apollo 20, however, and a great deal of development was already in progress for exended stays on the lunar surface beyond that.

That evolution in capability began with Apollo 12 in November 1969, when Conrad and Bean spent more than 31 hours on the surface supporting two

Below: President Nixon greets the astronauts back on Earth, his enthusiasm belying a reluctance to continue with Apollo. The last Moon mission was postponed until after his re-election in November 1972, to avoid embarrassment to his administration, should it be a catastrophic failure.

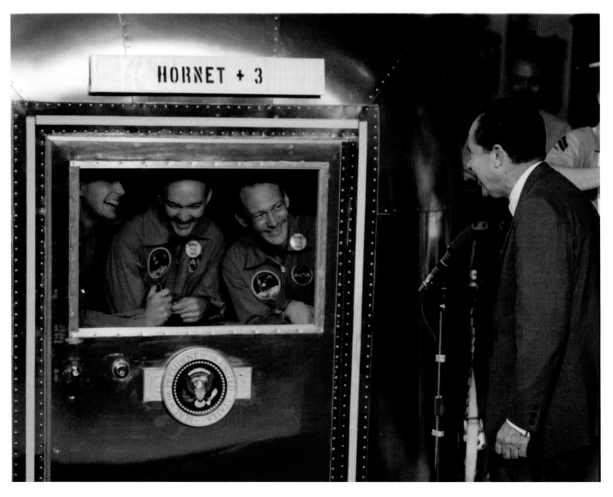

Above: *The Mobile Quarantine Facility (MQF), home for the three astronauts until delivered to Ellington Air Force Base, Texas, where they were transferred to the Lunar Receiving Laboratory for isolation to check for Moon bugs. None were detected.*

WAS LIFE FOUND ON THE MOON?

Rumours of Moon bugs or the propagation effect on the lunar environment are not unknown. When Apollo 12's crew returned with pieces of the robot Surveyor III, close to which they landed in November 1969, it was thought that germs from a technician had got past the sterilization procedures when the spacecraft was built and onto some of its components. Those components were analyzed, and spores of *Streptococcus mitis* were found in an enlarged and expanding colony. Science journals and space pundits continued to muse over this wondrous phenomenon – until more than 40 years later it was realized that sloppy contamination protection had infected the parts brought back, and the germs had been introduced after the components were returned to Earth, not before they went to the Moon!

Moonwalks while Dick Gordon orbited above. In April 1970, Apollo 13's Lovell, Swigert and Haise limped back to Earth after a near-catastrophic loss of the Service Module, with their Lunar Module serving as a lifeboat and no possibility of a Moon landing. Launched in January 1971, Apollo 14 saw Alan Shepard and Stuart Roosa land for 33 hours and conduct two Moonwalks while Edgar Mitchell remained in orbit. All these were H-series missions as defined by Owen Maynard's classification of capabilities.

By 1971 NASA had been unable to obtain funds to prevent cancellation of two Moon missions, a third Saturn V being taken for the launch of the Skylab space station, so only three more landings remained. These were classified as J-series flights and each placed two astronauts on the surface for 66–74 hours, supporting three Moonwalks and utilizing a roving vehicle to travel far from base. Each of those missions returned 170–242lb (77–110kg) of samples.

Launched in July 1971, Apollo 15 sent Dave Scott and Jim Irwin to the Moon, with Alfred Worden in orbit, followed by John Young and Charlie Duke, with Stuart Roosa in orbit on Apollo 16 in April 1972. Eugene Cernan and geology Harrison Schmitt flew the last mission to the Moon, with Ronald Evans staying in orbit, during Apollo 17 in December 1972.

Only 12 Apollo astronauts walked on the Moon and no one has been back since. It was not meant to be that way when the programme began. Scientists and engineers imagined that this was the start of an expanding endeavour to explore the solar system with astronauts – but politicians and the general public saw Apollo 11 as the finishing flag in a race against an ideological adversary, rather than the beginning of an unprecedented period of human exploration defined by scientific research stations on the Moon and Mars. Those who thought it was a race were satisfied that it had been run and won; those who wanted more are still waiting.

However, there was a colossal legacy from the six Apollo Moon landings. The technology developed for the Moon programme ensured a solid foundation

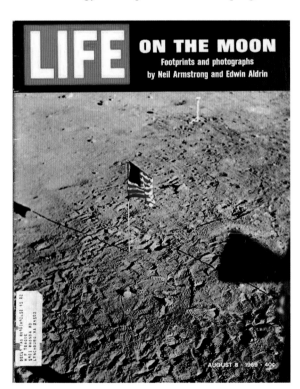

Opposite: *Celebrations break out in Mission Control after they see a sign saying "Mission Accomplished" on one of the large screens.*

Left: Life *magazine had followed the space programme from the outset, signing an exclusive deal with the first seven astronauts selected for the Mercury programme in 1959. They were there when the goal was achieved.*

Left: *The ticker-tape parade in New York brought hundreds of thousands of citizens out to celebrate the safe return of the crew and the accomplishment of a centuries-old dream of flying to the Moon.*

for successive generations of human space flight initiatives, including the Space Shuttle, which saw 135 launches between 1981 and 2011, and the International Space Station which was assembled as part of a collaborative effort between the United States, Europe, Japan, Canada and Russia (the ideological adversary that had triggered Apollo) and has been permanently manned since 2000.

Equally important, some would say more so, was the stimulation to an environmental awareness, triggered in part by Barbara Ward's seminal book *Only One Earth*, with its cover image of the Earth in the blackness of space. From that technological rebound grew an awareness that spread in the 1970s across the United States, Europe and the rest of the world – namely, that our own planet is more precious to us than any other.

This is a largely unrecognized legacy, growing with the later realization that advanced technology is vital for the human race to better define the harm being done to Earth by profligate abuse of the environment. The real enduring legacy of Apollo, this awareness of our true place in the cosmos and knowledge about our Earth can inform intelligent applications aiming at a more equitable balance for all living things on this most precious of all worlds in the solar system. Without going to the Moon, we would never have discovered the Earth.

Above: *The legacy of Apollo resides in the International Space Station, permanently manned since the year 2000, and supported by teams of astronauts from the United States, Russia, Europe, Japan and Canada.*

Opposite: *Media interest reached fever pitch as print and electronic outlets went "Moon mad"!*

FACTS & FIGURES

APOLLO MISSIONS 7-17

Table 1: Mission Type

Destination	Earth orbit	Lunar Orbit/Fly-by	Lunar landing	Lunar Roving Vehicle
Apollo 7	X			
Apollo 8		X		
Apollo 9	X			
Apollo 10		X		
Apollo 11			X	
Apollo 12			X	
Apollo 13		X		
Apollo 14			X	
Apollo 15			X	X
Apollo 16			X	X
Apollo 17			X	X

Note: Apollo 13 was a fly-by following the loss of power in the spacecraft.

Table 2: Crew Assignments

Seat Position	CDR	CMP	LMP
Apollo 7	Walter M. Schirra, Jr	Don F. Eisele	R. Walter Cunningham
Apollo 8	Frank F. Borman II	James A. Lovell, Jr	William A. Anders
Apollo 9	James A. McDivitt	David R. Scott	Russell L. Schweickart
Apollo 10	Thomas P. Stafford	John W. Young	Eugene A. Cernan
Apollo 11	Neil A. Armstrong	Michael Collins	Edwin W. Aldrin, Jr
Apollo 12	Charles Conrad, Jr	Richard F. Gordon, Jr	Alan L. Bean
Apollo 13	James A. Lovell, Jr	John L. Swigert, Jr	Fred W. Haise
Apollo 14	Alan B. Shepard, Jr	Stuart A. Roosa	Edgar D. Mitchell
Apollo 15	David R. Scott	Alfred M. Worden	James B. Irwin
Apollo 16	John W. Young	Thomas K. Mattingly II	Charles M. Duke, Jr
Apollo 17	Eugene A. Cernan	Ronald E. Evans	Harrison H. Schmitt

Note: CDR is Commander; CMP is Command Module Pilot, LMP is Lunar Module Pilot.

Table 3: Crew Information

Astronaut	Born	Selected	Number of Apollo flights	Age at flights
Aldrin	20 Jan 1930	1963	1	39
Anders	17 Oct 1933	1963	1	35
Armstrong	5 Aug 1930	1962	1	38
Bean	15 Mar 1932	1963	1	37
Borman II	28 Mar 1928	1962	1	40
Cernan	14 Mar 1934	1963	2	35 and 38
Collins	31 Oct 1930	1963	1	38
Conrad	2 Jun 1930	1962	1	39
Cunningham	16 Mar 1932	1963	1	35
Duke	3 Oct 1935	1966	1	36
Eisele	23 Jun 1930	1962	1	38
Evans	10 Nov 1933	1966	1	39
Gordon	5 Oct 1929	1963	1	40
Haise	14 Nov 1933	1966	1	36
Irwin	17 Mar 1930	1966	1	41
Lovell	25 Mar 1928	1963	2	40 and 42
Mattingly II	17 Mar 1936	1966	1	36
McDivitt	10 Jun 1929	1962	1	39
Mitchell	17 Sept 1930	1966	1	40
Roosa	16 Aug 1933	1966	1	37
Schirra	3 Sept 1923	1959	1	45
Schmitt	3 Jul 1935	1965	1	37
Schweickart	25 Oct 1935	1963	1	33
Scott	6 June 1930	1963	2	36 and 39
Shepard	18 Nov 1923	1959	1	47
Stafford	17 Sept 1930	1962	1	38
Swigert	30 Aug 1931	1966	1	38
Worden	7 Feb 1932	1966	1	39
Young	24 sept 1930	1962	2	38 and 41

HOW MUCH DID IT COST?

In the period 1960 to 1973, total US government expenditure amounted to $1,865,917,000, nearly $1,866 billion. Of that total, NASA spent $19.4 billion on the Apollo programme, about two-thirds of its (NASA's) budget over that period. This amounts to almost exactly 1% of all US government expenditure between 1960 and 1973. For the last 30 years NASA's budget has been less than half that each year.

Table 4: Flight Date, Duration, Time on the Surface and Spacewalks

Mission	Launch (yr:month:day)	Duration (hr:min:sec)	LM on surface (hr:min:sec)	Spacewalks
Apollo 7	68:10:11	260:09:03		
Apollo 8	68:12:21	147:00:42		
Apollo 9	69:03:03	241:00:54		
Apollo 10	69:05:18	192:03:23		
Apollo 11	69:07:21	195:18:35	21:36:21	1
Apollo 12	69:11:14	244:36:25	31:31:12	2
Apollo 13	70:04:11	142:54:41		
Apollo 14	71:01:31	216:01:58	33:30:31	
Apollo 15	71:07:26	295:11:53	66:54:54	4*
Apollo 16	72:04:16	265:51:05	71:02:13	4*
Apollo 17	72:12:07	301:51:59	74:59:39	4*

Note: Launch date is local time; * indicates missions in which the Command Module Pilot conducted an EVA to retrieve science packages.

Table 5: Lunar Landing Date, Total Lunar Spacewalk Duration and Lunar Samples Retrieved

Mission	Landing Date (yr:month:day)	Spacewalk Duration (hr:min:sec)	Samples Retrieved (lb/kg)
Apollo 11	69:07:20	02:31:40	47.51/21.55
Apollo 12	69:11:19	07:45:18	75.73/34.35
Apollo 14	71:02:05	09:22:31	93.21/42.28
Apollo 15	71:07:30	18:34:46	170.44/77.31
Apollo 16	72:04:21	20:14:14	211.00/95.71
Apollo 17	72:12:11	22:03:57	243.65/110.52

Note: Landing date is in GMT time.

Table 6: Saturn V Launch Vehicle Stages

	S-IC	S-II	S-IVB
Length (ft/m)	138/42	81.5/24.84	58.3/17.77
Diameter (ft/m)	33/9.95	33/9.95	21.7/21.73
Weight dry (lb/kg)	288,750/130,977	79,918/36,250	25,000/11,340
Weight fuelled (lb/kg)	5,022,674/2,278,285	1,059,171/480.440	260,523/118,173
Engines	5 x F-1	5 x J-2	1 x J-2
Liquid oxygen (lb/litres)	3,307,855/1,311,000	821,022/85,793	192,023/20,107
RP-1 kerosene (lb/litres)	1,426,069/805,622	NA	NA
Liquid hydrogen (lb/kg)	NA	158,221/282,555	43,500/77,680
Total thrust (lb/kN)	7,653,854/34,044	1,157,707/5,149	203,779/906

Table 7: Where Are They Now?

Mission	Spacecraft	Current Location
Apollo 8	CSM-103	Museum of Science and Industry, Chicago, Illinois
Apollo 9	CSM-104	San Diego Air & Space Museum, California
Apollo 10	CSM-106	Science Museum, London
Apollo 11	CSM-107	On tour of the United States for the 50th anniversary
Apollo 12	CSM-108	Virginia Air & Space Center, Virginia
Apollo 13	CSM-109	Kansas Cosmosphere & Space Center, Texas
Apollo 14	CSM-110	Kennedy Space Center, Florida
Apollo 15	CSM-112	National Air and Space Museum, Dayton, Ohio
Apollo 16	CSM-113	US Space & Rocket Center, Huntsville, Alabama
Apollo 17	CSM-114	Space Center Houston, Texas

APOLLO 11 MISSIONS

Table 8: Apollo 11 Spacecraft

	Apollo Command Module	Apollo Service Module
Length (ft/m)	11.42/3.48	24.58/7.49
Diameter (ft/m)	12.83/3.91	12.83/3.91
Pressurized volume (cu ft/cu m)	366/10.4	NA
Launch weight (lb/kg)	12,250/5,557	54,060/24,522
Number of attitude control thrusters	12	16
Attitude thruster thrust per motor (lb/kN)	93/410	100/440
Thruster propellant loaded (lb/kg)	246/111.6	1,340/608
Thruster propellant remaining (lb/kg)	205/92.9	752/341
SPS engine thrust (lb/kN)		20,500/91
SPS propellant loaded (lb/kg)		40,803/18,508
SPS propellant remaining (lb/kg)		5,064/2,297
SPS delta velocity change (ft/sec;m/sec)		9,200/2,800
Electrical power	5 x silver-zinc batteries	3 x fuel cells
Power level	3 x 40amp/hr/2 x 0.75 amp/hr	1.4kW, 30vdc
Drinking water capacity (lb/kg)		33/15
Waste water capacity (lb/kg)		58/26
Cryogenic hydrogen loaded (lb/kg)		54.1/24.54
Cryogenic hydrogen remaining (lb/kg)		19.2/8.71
Cryogenic oxygen loaded (lb/kg)		615/279
Cryogenic oxygen remaining (lb/kg)		261/118.4

Note: Cryogenic reactants were carried for use in the fuel cells for electrical power from the three fuel cells, with oxygen used as well for the crew to breathe. Quantities shown as "Remaining" are those at the end of mission for that element of the spacecraft.

Table 9: Lunar Module

	Lunar Module Ascent Stage	Lunar Module Descent Stage
Height (ft/m)	9.3/2.83	10.6/3.23
Width (ft/m)	14.08/4.29	13.8/4.2
Width, landing gear extended (ft/m)		31/9.4
Pressurized volume (cu ft/cu m)	160/4.5	NA
Dry weight (lb/kg)	4,740/2,150	
Launch weight (lb/kg)	10,300/4,700	22,783/10,334
Number of attitude control thrusters	16	
Attitude thruster thrust per motor	100/440	
Thruster propellant loaded (lb/kg)	634/287.5	
Thruster propellant remaining (lb/kg)	315/142.9	
DPS engine thrust (lb/kN)		10,125/45,040
DPS propellant loaded (lb/kg)		18,184/8,248
DPS propellant remaining (lb/kg)		770/349
DPS delta velocity change (ft/sec;m/sec)		8,100/2,500
APS engine thrust (lb/kN)	3,500/16	
APS propellant loaded (lb/kg)	5,238/2,376	
APS propellant remaining (lb/kg)	402/182	
APS delta velocity change (ft/sec;m/sec)	7,280/2,220	
Thrust/weight ratio at lunar lift-off	2.124/1	
Electrical power	2 x silver-zinc batteries	4 x silver-zinc batteries
Power level	28-32vdc, 296amp/hr	28-32vdc, 415amp/hr
Water capacity (lb/kg)	85/38.5	217/98.4
Water remaining (lb/kg)	47.5/21.5	70.5/32
Oxygen loaded (lb/kg)	5/2.27	48.2/21.8
Oxygen remaining (lb/kg)	3.9/1.77	31/14.1

Note: Quantities shown as "Remaining" are those at the end of mission for that element of the spacecraft.

Below: *In the loneliness of Tranquility Base, the TV camera sits on its tripod (left) while the flag stands erect in the dusty surface (right).*

Table 10: Menu for Armstrong

Meal	Days 1 and 5	Day 2	Day 3	Day 4
A	Peaches	Fruit cocktail	Peaches	Bacon & applesauce
	Bacon squares (8)	Sausage patties	Bacon squares (8)	Sugar coated corn flakes
	Strawberry cubes	Toasted bread cubes	Apricot cereal cubes	Peanut cubes
	Grape drink	Cocoa	Grape drink	Cocoa
B	Beef & potatoes	Frankfurters	Chicken soup	Shrimp cocktail
	Butterscotch pudding	Applesauce	Turkey & gravy	Ham & potatoes
	Brownies	Chocolate pudding	Cheese cracker cubes	Fruit cocktail
	Grape punch	Orange-grapefruit drink	Chocolate cubes	Date fruitcake
			Pineapple-grapefruit drink	Grapefruit drink
C	Salmon salad	Spaghetti/meat sauce	Tuna salad	Beef stew
	Chicken & rice	Pork & scallop potatoes	Chicken stew	Coconut cubes
	Sugar cookie cubes	Pineapple fruitcake	Butterscotch pudding	Banana pudding
	Cocoa	Grape punch	Cocoa	Grape punch
	Pineapple grapefruit drink	Grapefruit drink		

Note: Day 1 consists of Meal B and C only.

Table 11: Crew Data

	Armstrong	Collins	Aldrin
Born	Aug 5, 1930	Oct 31, 1930	Jan 20, 1930
Hair	Blonde	Brown	Blonde
Eyes	Blue	Brown	Blue
Height (in/cm)	71/180	71/180	70/178
Weight (lb/kg)	165/74.8	165/74.8	165/74.8
Children	2	3	3
Children's ages in July 1969 (yrs)	12/6	10/7/6	13/11/11
Service	Civilian	US Air Force	US Air Force
Rank	Test pilot	Colonel	Colonel
Selected as astronaut	Sep 1962	Oct 1963	Oct 1963
Previous flights	Gemini VIII	Gemini X	Gemini XII
Annual pay (in 1969/ in 2019 money)	$30,054/$210,378	$17,147/$120,000	$18,622/$130,354

Note: The average wage in 2019 is based on an inflation factor of 700% since 1969. Exchange rate values show that in 1969 Armstrong's salary was £12,000 in UK currency, his 2019 salary equivalent to £162,000 at 2018 exchange rates.

INDEX

PICTURE CREDITS

The publisher would like to thank the following for kindly allowing their pictures to be reproduced in this book (key: t=top, b=bottom, l=left, r=right).

AC Electronics: 132tr, 132b, 133l, 133r.

Avco: 65.

D. Meltzer: 46.

David Baker: 9, 14, 17, 18, 20–1, 22, 23t, 34, 50, 108, 118, 121, 158.

Eberhard Max: 16.

Gdansk National Museum of Poland: 23b.

Getty Images: 29.

Grumman: 109, 116.

Hamish Lindsay: 94.

MIT: 85, 91.

NASA: 2, 4–5, 6, 8, 15, 24–5, 33, 35t, 37, 39, 41, 42, 43, 44, 45, 47, 48, 49, 51, 52, 53, 54–5, 56, 57, 59, 60t, 60b, 61, 63, 64, 66t, 66b, 67, 68t, 68b, 70, 71, 72, 73t, 73b, 74, 75, 76t, 76b, 77, 78, 79, 80t, 80b, 81, 82, 83, 84t, 84b, 86, 87, 89, 90b, 93, 96, 97, 98–9, 101, 102, 103, 104, 105t, 105b, 106, 107, 110, 111, 112, 113t, 113b, 114, 115, 117, 119t, 119b, 120, 122, 123, 124, 125t, 125b, 126t, 126b, 127, 128, 129t, 129b, 130, 131, 132tl, 134t, 134b, 135t, 136, 137, 138, 139t, 140, 141, 142, 143, 144, 145, 146, 147, 149, 151, 152, 153, 154, 155, 156–7, 159, 160, 161, 162, 163, 164–5, 166–7, 168, 169, 170, 172–3, 174–5, 176, 177, 178, 179, 180–1, 182, 183, 188.

NASA–Bill Anders: 92.

NASA–MSFC: 28, 32t, 32b.

NASA–Oona Raisanen: 135b.

North American Aviation: 69, 90t, 139b.

Novosti: 13.

Rocketdyne: 36, 38t, 38b.

Rolls-Royce: 35b.

Sergei Arssenev: 19.

USAF: 30, 31.

US Army: 26, 27.

US Congress: 10–11.

White House: 40.